Multiple-choice tests in advanced mathematics

Multiple-choice tests in advanced mathematics

Charles Plumpton, Ph.D.

Moderator in Mathematics, University of London School Examinations Board; formerly Reader in Engineering Mathematics, Queen Mary College, University of London

Eva Shipton, B.Sc.

Formerly Teacher-moderator in Advanced-level Mathematics, University of London School Examinations Board; Chief Examiner A/O Mathematics, University of London School Examinations Board; formerly Deputy Head, Owen's School, Potters Bar

SECOND EDITION

M
MACMILLAN

A note on using this book

The rubrics for answering questions in the various sections of the tests do *not* precede each section as they would do in real examination papers. Instead, in order to conserve space in the book, a pull-out section with rubrics printed on it is included at the end. When the book is being used the pull-out can be kept extended and the rubrics read by the student as needed as he/she works through the tests.

This is a practical if unusual approach and one that saves considerable repetition and wasted space in the main body of the book.

First edition 1983
Reprinted 1984
Second edition 1985

Published by
MACMILLAN EDUCATION LTD
Houndmills, Basingstoke, Hampshire RG21 2XS
and London
Companies and representatives
throughout the world

Printed in Hong Kong

British Library Cataloguing in Publication Data
Plumpton, C.
Multiple-choice tests in advanced mathematics—2nd ed.
1. Mathematics——Examinations, questions, etc.
I. Title II. Shipton, E.
510′.76 QA43
ISBN 0–333–39822–X

Preface

For some years, multiple-choice questions have been used in some GCE A-level examinations in mathematics. There is, therefore, a great need for specimen questions and papers of this type for use in mock examinations and the general preparation of A-level students, in addition to the past papers of the GCE boards, where these are available. Further, the acceptance by the GCE boards of 'common-core' based syllabuses in unified 'modern-traditional' mathematics at A-level, and the use of 'no-choice' examination papers implies that students ought to cover the new syllabus completely. No longer can some topics be conveniently ignored, particularly as university departments in pure and applied science are tending to assume a thorough knowledge of the 'common-core' syllabus allied to a sound competence in manipulative skills.

This book is particularly aimed at students preparing for the new A-level Syllabus B subjects, Mathematics, Further Mathematics, Pure Mathematics, Applied Mathematics, and Pure Mathematics with Statistics first examined by the London GCE Board in June 1982, but should be of great value to students taking the A-level examinations of other boards, particularly those which include a multiple-choice element.

There is a further use for the question papers in this book. Multiple-choice papers are designed to give a good coverage of the syllabus. It is felt, therefore, that, whether or not multiple-choice papers form part of an examination, a student preparing for any GCE A-level examination in mathematics or any future examination at this level, particularly one based on a unified approach, would find it helpful to use these papers as revision exercises, noting the questions which prove difficult and thus reinforcing the need to revise particular areas of the syllabus.

Many of the questions in this book have been pretested at Owen's School by a group of pupils entered for the June 1982 examination. This is, of course, very limited pretesting but, on the other hand, both authors have been involved in the setting and moderation of A-level multiple-choice questions from the time when this type of paper was first introduced by the London Board. This means that they have looked at literally hundreds of questions with a critical eye and they feel that this experience has enabled them to set well-balanced papers with questions carefully graded for degree of difficulty.

Tests 1–8 contain only questions on 'pure' mathematics and are intended for students entered for an examination with a 'common-core' element. Tests 9–12 on Further Mathematics, containing both pure and applied items, and Tests 13 and 14, containing applied items only, are intended for more advanced students and contain some more difficult questions. Nevertheless, a time limit of $1\frac{1}{4}$ hours should be allowed for each test.

The general philosophy, jargon, etc. of multiple-choice questions is discussed in the introduction to the O-level book, *Multiple Choice Mathematics* by C. Plumpton (Macmillan Education, 1981), and will not be repeated here. The simple multiple-choice and multiple-completion item types of the O-level book occur here also, but in Tests 9–14 of this book additional item types are introduced. These are relationship analysis (Section III), data necessity (Section IV) and data sufficiency (Section V) items. These items enable coverage of topics which are difficult or unfair to examine by longer structured questions. Indeed, these more sophisticated item types are a far better test of mathematical understanding than some longer questions in which candidates may be applying a method or technique which they have learnt but have not properly understood. Section III (relationship analysis) tests insight into the relationship between mathematical statements in a way which is not covered by any other type of question. Both the Section IV (data necessity) and Section V (data sufficiency) items enable the candidate to show ability in analysing a question without the 'slog' of working it out. They also provide some training in such considerations as the dimensions of an answer, thus helping candidates to avoid some of the grosser errors met with in answers to conventional Applied Mathematics questions.

If candidates are given these papers to work through on a regular basis during the second year of their course, it will be found that this provides invaluable revision work as it will keep all the syllabus topics constantly under review. It is, indeed, hoped that each question paper in this book can be used as a specimen paper in relation to the multiple-choice papers of the London A-level Mathematics Syllabus B examination.

In this second edition of the book, a section has been added on the techniques of answering multiple-choice questions. Each question type is taken in turn and the various methods of approach discussed and illustrated with a wide variety of examples. On the whole, the item types known as simple multiple-choice and multiple-completion are illustrated by examples from the core syllabus, while examples from Applied Mathematics and Further Mathematics are used to illustrate the more sophisticated item types, namely relationship analysis, data necessity, and data sufficiency. This section should prove valuable to both teachers and students, particularly, in the latter case, to those who are working on their own.

Charles Plumpton
Eva Shipton

Answering techniques for multiple-choice questions

Because multiple-choice papers consist of a large number of questions, the time allowance for each question is severely limited and speed is essential. It is necessary, therefore, to recognize any short cuts and this is really tantamount to cultivating the ability to grasp the essentials of a question immediately. In the examples which now follow we examine each type of question in detail to show how speed and accuracy can be achieved.

I Simple multiple-choice

In this type of question the straightforward approach of working a question quickly and comparing one's answer with those supplied is sometimes the best method. This is particularly so in questions with numerical answers. However, there are many questions in which insight into the fundamentals enables one to discard many of the answers given or may direct one immediately to the correct answer. The following examples illustrate these different methods of approach.

1 *Straightforward working of the question*

Example 1

$$z = \text{i}\,(\sqrt{3} + \text{i})$$

$$\Rightarrow \quad \arg z =$$

A $\dfrac{2\pi}{3}$

B $\dfrac{5\pi}{6}$

C $-\dfrac{\pi}{6}$

D $\dfrac{\pi}{3}$

E $-\dfrac{\pi}{3}$

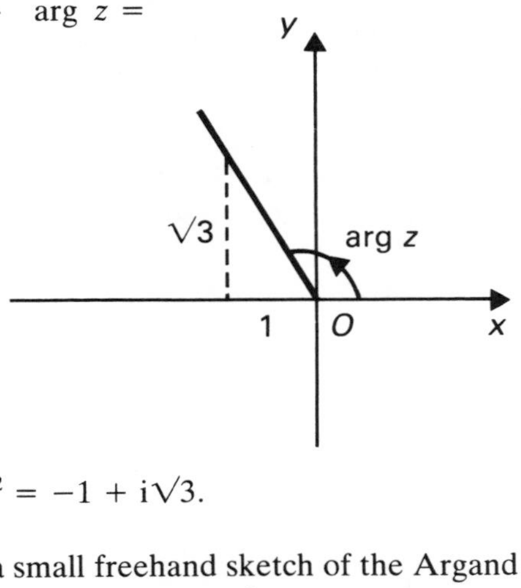

Simplifying,

$z = \text{i}\sqrt{3} + \text{i}^2 = -1 + \text{i}\sqrt{3}.$

Then, using a small freehand sketch of the Argand diagram, we see that $\arg z = \dfrac{2\pi}{3}$.

Hence the key is **A**.

Example 2 The coefficient of x^2 in the expansion of $(1 - 4x)^{1/4}$ in ascending powers of x, where $|x| < \frac{1}{4}$, is

A $-\dfrac{5}{2}$

B $\dfrac{5}{2}$

C $-\dfrac{3}{2}$

D $\dfrac{3}{2}$

E $-\dfrac{3}{32}$

For $(1 - 4x)^{-1/4}$ the term in x^2 is

$$\frac{(-\frac{1}{4}) \times (-\frac{5}{4})}{1 \times 2}(-4x)^2$$

$$= \frac{5x^2}{2} \quad \Rightarrow \quad \text{coefficient of } x^2 = \frac{5}{2}.$$

Hence the key is **B**.

Note: it is worth noticing that the expansion of $(1 + ax)^n$ where a and n are both negative is a series of positive terms.

2 *Factual recall*

Sometimes the examiner is simply testing whether your remember a fact or a formula, as in the following question.

Example 3 All solutions of the equation $\sin\theta = \sin\alpha$ are given by taking all integer values of n in $\theta =$

A $2n\pi \pm \alpha$

B $2n\pi + \alpha$

C $n\pi + (-1)^n\alpha$

D $n\pi + \alpha$

E $n\pi \pm \alpha$

You should know the formula so that you are able to write down **C** immediately and pass on to the next question. However, if you are confused and not sure, test each of the answers in a diagram until you come to the correct one. For instance, **A** clearly gives only first and fourth quadrant angles which is no good as we want first and second quadrant angles for sine. Continue in this way until you come to the correct key. This gives us another useful technique, that of trial and error.

3 *Trial and error*

This method has been seen to be useful for testing a formula of which one is not sure. It can also be used when the actual working out of a problem would be long, or difficult, or both.

Example 4

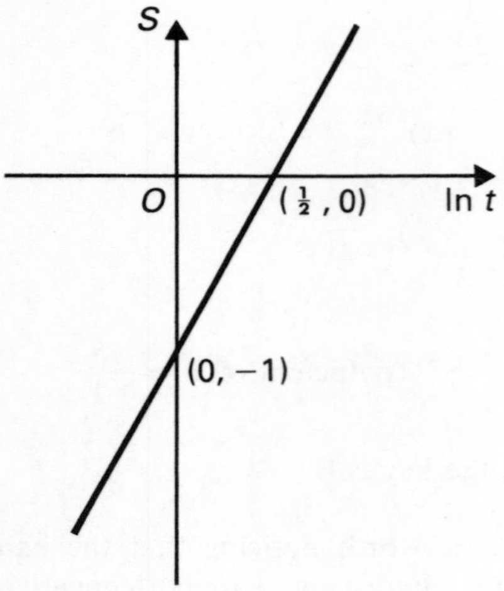

S is a linear function of $\ln t$ as shown. Which one of the following describes the relationship between S and t?

A $S = e^{1/2}e^{t/2}$

B $S = e^2e^{2t}$

C $t = e^2e^{2S}$

D $t = e^{1/2}e^{S/2}$

E none of the above

This could be done by obtaining the equation of the line passing through the two given points. However, it is probably simpler to test each of the two points in each of the equations until the equation which is satisfied by both is found.

$(\frac{1}{2}, 0) \;\Rightarrow\; t = e^{1/2}, S = 0,$
$(0, -1) \;\Rightarrow\; t = 1, S = -1.$

Trying the answers in turn:
In **A**, $S = 0$ gives no value for t, so no good.
In **B**, $S = 0$ also gives no value for t, so no good.
In **C**, $S = 0$ gives $t = e^2$, so no good.
In **D**, $S = 0$ gives $t = e^{1/2}$, correct and $S = -1$ gives $t = 1$, correct. Hence the key is **D**.

4 *Elimination of some answers*

This can be done for a variety of reasons, leaving fewer to consider or only one which is the correct key.

Example 5 $\frac{d}{dx}(3^x) =$

A 3^x

B 3^{x-1}

C $x3^{x-1}$

D $3^x \ln 3$

E $x \ln 3$

$\frac{dx}{d}(a^x)$ should, of course, be known but it is frequently forgotten. Most students, however, would recognize that logarithmic differentiation is necessary, which means that one can discard **A**, **B**, **C**. Of the two remaining, **E** is a simple linear expression and so can be discarded, leaving **D** as the key.

5 *Partial working of the problem*

Often some work on the original data enables one to eliminate some of the possible answers, as in the last question. This can mean that it is unnecessary to work out the whole problem.

Example 6 A straight line is obtained when y is plotted against $\ln x$. The relation between y and x is of the form, where k and n are constants,

A $y = k\,e^x$

B $y = e^x + k$

C $y = x^n + k$

D $e^y = x^n + k$

E $e^y = kx^n$

From the data we see that $y = a \ln x + b$. Comparing this with the answers given, **A**, **B** and **C** can be discarded at once, leaving just **D** and **E** from which to choose. As **E** gives $y \ln (kx^n) = \ln k + n \ln x$, this is clearly the required form and so is the correct key.

Example 7

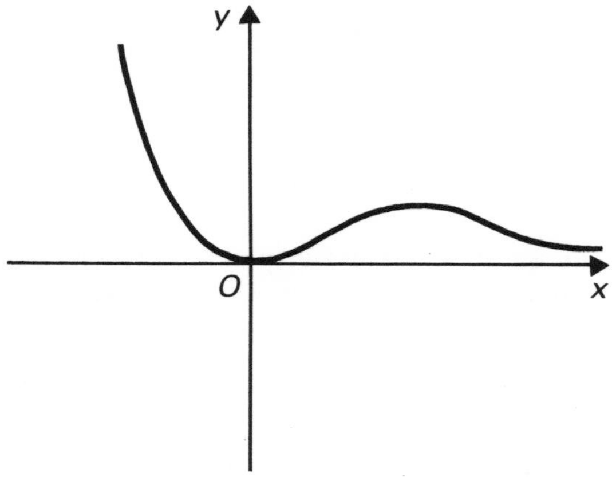

The sketch could be the graph of

A $y = x\,e^{-x}$

B $y = (\ln x)^2$

C $y = e^{-x^2}$

D $y = x^2\,e^{-x}$

E $y = x^2 \ln x$

In this type of question, note the main features of the graph and, starting with the easiest ones, see whether any of the answers can be eliminated. In this case, the curve passes through the origin, which means that **B** and **C** can be discarded. Secondly, $y \geqslant 0$ for all x, which means that **A** can be discarded. The choice is then between **D** and **E** but **E** is not possible as $\ln x$ is not defined for $x < 0$. Hence the key is **D**. Notice that we have not had to embark on the time-consuming differentiation to check for the turning points.

II Multiple-completion

In this type of question some information is given and, then, three different assertions are made, relating to the information. The candidate is required to investigate each of these assertions to find whether it is correct or not.

It will usually be found that the three statements have a common theme and, often, a little work done on the data will give all the answers. It is also worth noticing that not all the logical possibilities are present in the keys. Thus, **2** only or **1** and **3** only are not possible keys. This means that when **1** is incorrect then **3** must be correct.

If **1** is correct, key cannot be **C** or **E**.

If **1** is incorrect, and **2** is incorrect, key must be **E**.

If **1** is incorrect, and **2** is correct, key must be **C**.

The following examples illustrate these principles.

Example 8 A particle moves on the x-axis so that its distance x metres from the origin at time t seconds is given by $x = 1 + 3\cos(2t + \pi/4)$.

1 Its speed is greatest when $t = 0$

2 $|\text{Acceleration}| = 4|x|$

3 The maximum value of x is 4

The work to be done on the data is simply to differentiate twice to find the velocity and acceleration. Thus

$$x = 1 + 3\cos(2t + \pi/4),$$
$$\dot{x} = -6\sin(2t + \pi/4),$$
$$\ddot{x} = -12\cos(2t + \pi/4).$$

As the maximum value of $\dot{x}$ is given by $\ddot{x} = 0$, **1** is clearly incorrect. Inspection shows that **2** is also incorrect. It follows that the key is **E**.

Sometimes one of the three statements may strike you as obviously correct or incorrect. In this case you should start with that one, as in the following example.

Example 9 The equation $3x^3 + 4x^2 - 5x - 1 = 0$

1 has a root between -2 and -3

2 has a root between 0 and 1

3 has only two real roots

Clearly, **3** is incorrect as a cubic equation can have three real roots or only one and so it cannot have two real roots. As **3** is incorrect, it follows that **1** must be correct, so that it is only necessary to test **2** and we see that $f(0) = -1$, $f(1) = 1$ so that there is a root between 0 and 1 and this means that **2** is correct and so the key is **B**.

Example 10 The position vector of the point P is $\mathbf{r}$, and s, t are parameters.

1 When $\mathbf{r} = s\mathbf{i} + t\mathbf{j}$, the locus of P is a straight line

2 When $\mathbf{r}.\mathbf{i} = \mathbf{j}.\mathbf{j}$, the locus of P is a plane

3 When $\mathbf{r}.\mathbf{r} = \mathbf{j}.\mathbf{j}$, the locus of P is a sphere

This question concerns recognizing formulae written in terms of vectors. Looking at **1**, students should recognize the fact that when a straight line is written in parametric form only *one* parameter is necessary so that **1** is incorrect. *No further* working is necessary on this. (In fact, the equation represents the x–y plane.) Looking at **2** we note that, as $\mathbf{j}.\mathbf{j} = 1$, the equation is $\mathbf{r}.\mathbf{i} = 1$, which should be recognized as the perpendicular form of the equation of a plane. Hence the key is **C**, as it follows that if **1** is incorrect and **2** correct, then **3** must be correct.

Note on vector equations: many A-level students feel insecure when dealing with vector equations. If this is the case, remember that these equations may be easily transformed to cartesian equations by expressing the variable **r** as $\mathbf{r} = x\mathbf{i} + y\mathbf{i} + z\mathbf{k}$. If this is done, the above equations become

1 $z = 0$, **2** $x = 1$, **3** $x^2 + y^2 + z^2 = 1$;

i.e. the equations of a plane, plane and sphere.

Example 11

$$I = \int_1^2 \frac{1}{1+x}\,dx \,.$$

J is an estimate of I using the trapezium rule with two strips,
K is an estimate of I using the trapezium rule with four strips.

1 $J > I$

2 $J > K$

3 $I = \ln(3/2)$

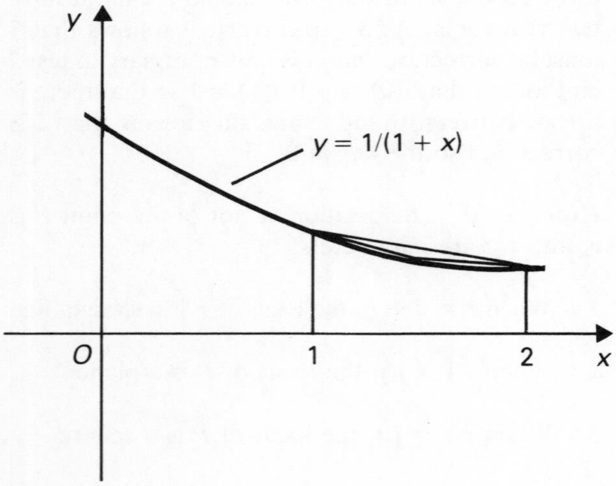

A diagram is helpful here. The concavity shows that **1** and **2** are both true. Integrating gives

$$I = \Big[\ln(x+1)\Big]_1^2 = \ln(3/2)$$

and so **3** is correct.
Hence the key is **A**.

Example 12 The circle $x^2 + y^2 + 4x - 6y + 4 = 0$

1 has centre $(-2, 3)$

2 touches the x-axis

3 does not cut the y-axis

In this question a rearrangement of the equation of the circle enables us to answer to the whole question. Writing the equation as

$$(x+2)^2 + (y-3)^2 = 9$$

gives the centre as $(-2, 3)$ and makes it easy to see that **2** is correct. Then, putting $x = 0$ gives $(y-3)^2 = 5$, which has real roots (no need to find) so that **3** is incorrect and the key is **B**.

III Relationship analysis

It is important to note that in this type of question you are not being asked to decide the truth or otherwise of the statements made, but merely the logical relationship between them. This is illustrated in the very simple examples 13 to 16.

Example 13

1 $x = 3$

2 $x > 2$

As $3 > 2$, it is clear that **1** implies **2** or **1**$\Rightarrow$ **2**. But **2** does not imply **1**, i.e. $x > 2$ does not necessarily mean that x must be equal to 3. This can readily be seen if we take a particular value, say $x = 2\frac{1}{2}$, which satisfies **2** but not **1**.

This method of disproving a proposition by finding a single case for which it is not true is called proof by counter-example. Notice that it is sufficient to find just one counter-example in order to disprove a proposition.

Example 14

1 $x^2 < 1$

2 $-1 < x < 1$

In this example **1** implies **2** since, if $x^2 < 1$, x must be a number numerically less than 1, i.e. $-1 < x < 1$. It is also true that **2** implies **1**, since if a number is numerically less than 1 then its square is less than 1. So we have **1** $\Leftrightarrow$ **2**, which gives key **C**.

Example 15

1 $x = 1$

2 $x > 2$

As $1 < 2$, it follows that **1** denies **2** and also that **2** denies **1**. Hence the key is **D**.

Example 16

1 $x > 1$

2 $x < 5$

In this example, **1** and **2** are unrelated. A number greater than 1 *could* be less than 5, but it could also be greater than 5. Also, a number less than 5 *could* be greater than 1, but it could also be less than 1. Hence the key is **E**.

In the more difficult examples it is essential that the meaning of each statement is completely understood.

Example 17 f(x) is a differentiable function when $x = a$.

1 f(x) has a minimum value when $x = a$

2 $f'(a) = 0$, $f''(a) > 0$

A differentiable function has a minimum value at a point where its gradient is zero and that gradient has changed in sign, from negative before the critical point to positive after it. This *generally* means that the gradient is steadily increasing, so that $f'(a) = 0$, $f''(a) > 0$, is sufficient to determine a minimum value. Hence **2** ⇒ **1**.

However, it is possible for the gradient or derived function itself to have a stationary value, a point of inflexion, at the critical point, in which case $f''(a) = 0$ but $x = a$ still gives a minimum value. [$f(x) \equiv x^4$ is an example of this, where $f'(0) = 0$, $f''(0) = 0$ but $x = 0$ gives a minimum value.]

Hence **1** ⇏ **2** and the key is **B**.

Example 18

1 Two events X and Y are mutually exclusive

2 $Y = X'$

Mutually exclusive events are events which cannot occur simultaneously. A Venn diagram often clarifies this type of question, and here we get:

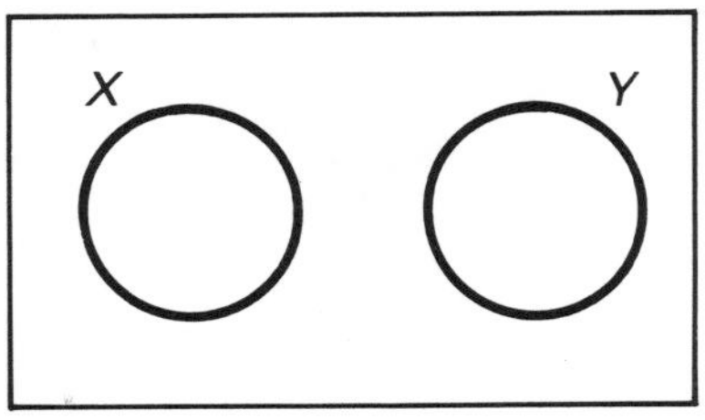

This means that X and Y are mutually exclusive

$$\Rightarrow \quad X \cap Y = \phi\,.$$

Clearly, from the diagram, Y is not necessarily equal to X' and so **1** ⇏ **2**. However, as $X \cap X' = \phi$ it does follow that X and X' are mutually exclusive events and so **2** ⇒ **1**. Hence the key is **B**.

Notice that you need to be on the alert for any special cases or exceptions to a general rule. The implication sign in **1** ⇒ **2** does not mean that *usually* this is so but that it is *always* so. Hence, even a single exception can destroy an implication.

Example 19

1 **a** and **b** are perpendicular vectors

2 **a.b** = 0

Clearly **1** ⇒ **2** as this is the condition for perpendicularity and, generally speaking, **2** would imply **1**, but there is the possibility that **a** or **b** is a zero vector which would also give **a.b** = 0, and so **2** ⇏ **1** and the key is **A**. Usually a question such as this would be prefaced with the information that **a** and **b** are non-zero vectors, in which case the key would be **C**.

Example 20 $f(x) \equiv x^3 + 3ax + b; \qquad a, b \in \mathbb{R}\,.$

1 $a > 0$

2 $f(x) = 0$ has three real, distinct roots

This question requires an understanding of the nature of the roots of a cubic equation. Graphically, the case of three real, distinct roots shows as:

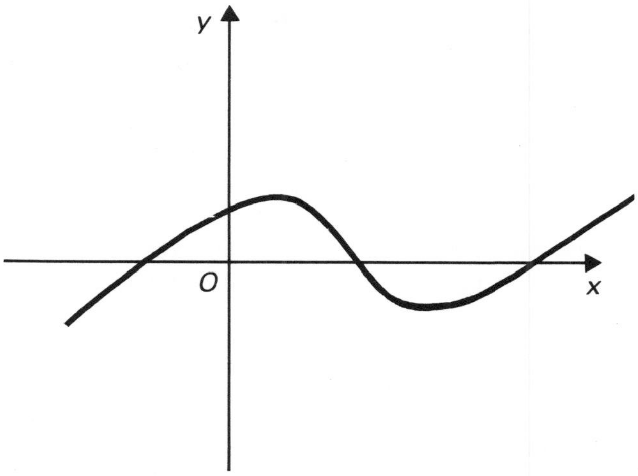

This means that the function has maximum and minimum values of opposite sign. The values of x at these turning points are given by $f'(x) = 0$, i.e.

$$3x^2 + 3a = 0 \;\Rightarrow\; x^2 = -a \,.$$

Thus there can only be turning points when $a < 0$, and this means that **1** denies **2** and **2** denies **1**, giving key **D**.

Probably the key which is most often ignored in this type of question is **E**. Remember the point made at the beginning of this section, that you are not testing the truth of the statements made but the possibility of implication between them.

Example 21

1 $|x| < 3$

2 $|x-3| < 1$

The solution set of the first inequality can be written down at sight as $\{x : -3 < x < 3\}$. For the solution set of the second, the limiting values are clearly 2 and 4, giving -1 and 1 respectively for $(x-3)$; thus the solution set is $\{x : 2 < x < 4\}$. Examining these two solution sets we see that there is no implication between **1** and **2**. For some values of x both are true, e.g. $\{x : 2 < x < 3\}$; for some **1** is true but not **2**, e.g. $\{x : -3 < x < 2\}$; for some **2** is true but not **1**, e.g. $\{x : 3 < x < 4\}$. Hence the key is **E**.

This could also be shown by counter-examples without finding the solution sets and students could do this as an exercise. However, see the next example.

Example 22

1 $x(x+3) < 0$

2 $|x+1| < 2$

The solution set of **1** is $\{x : -3 < x < 0\}$; and of **2** is $\{x : -3 < x < 1\}$. Any value of x satisfying the first of these inequalities also also satisfies the second and so **1** $\Rightarrow$ **2**. There are, however, values of x which satisfy the second but do not satisfy the first and so **2** $\not\Rightarrow$ **1**. Thus the key is **A**.

The method of using a counter-example would serve for proving the non-implication but would not do to prove the implication.

IV Data necessity

This is probably the most difficult type of multiple-choice question as it requires a complete analysis of a question, usually without actually working it out. However, it is a good plan to ask oneself how one would set about the question and, sometimes, to write down essential equations.

Example 23 A ship, with position vector $\mathbf{r}_1$ at noon, moves with constant velocity $\mathbf{v}_1$. A second ship, with position vector $\mathbf{r}_2$ at noon, moves with constant velocity $\mathbf{v}_2$. Find whether the ships are on a collision course.

1 $\mathbf{r}_1$ is given

2 $\mathbf{r}_2$ is given

3 $\mathbf{v}_1 + \mathbf{v}_2$ is given

4 $\mathbf{v}_1 - \mathbf{v}_2$ is given

As $\mathbf{v}_1$ and $\mathbf{v}_2$ can be found from **3** and **4**, and $\mathbf{r}_1$ and $\mathbf{r}_2$ are given in **1** and **2**, it is tempting to say that all four are needed because, if we know the speed and course of each ship, we can solve the problem. However, we ought to investigate whether any of the information can be dispensed with. The method with this type of question would be to find the position at noon of the first ship relative to the second and then the velocity of the second ship relative to the first. Then, if this relative velocity is in the same direction as the relative position, the ships will collide. Hence, we need $\mathbf{r}_1 - \mathbf{r}_2$ and $\mathbf{v}_2 - \mathbf{v}_1$ which can be found from **1**, **2** and **4**, so that **3** is unnecessary and the key is **C**.

Example 24

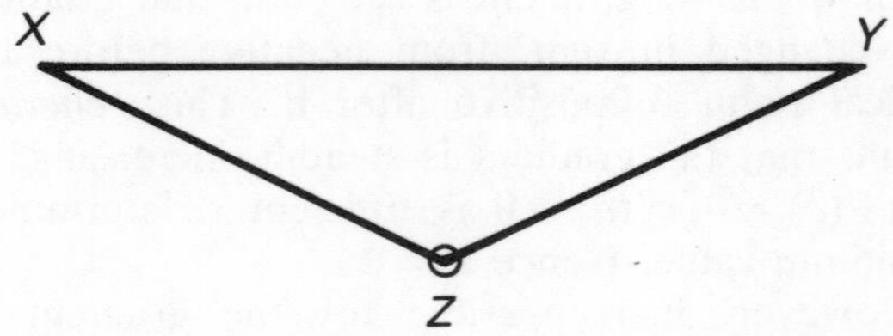

XZY is an elastic string, X and Y being on the same horizontal level. A smooth, heavy ring is threaded onto the string and hangs in equilibrium. Find the modulus of elasticity.

1 The weight of the ring is given

2 XY is given

3 The natural length of the string is given

4 XZ is given

The equation for the modulus is $T = \lambda x/l$ so that tension, extension and natural length are needed to find the modulus.

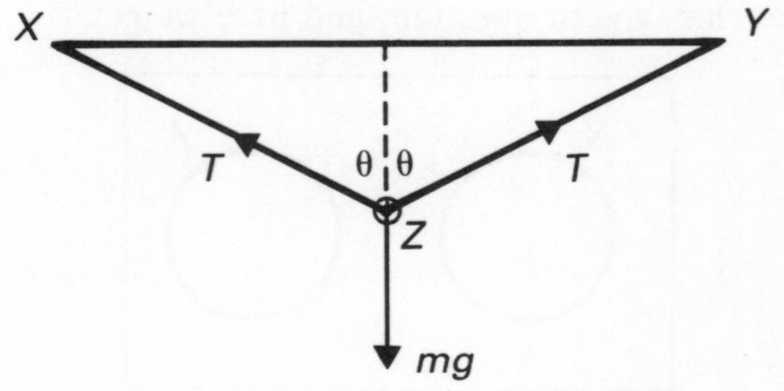

As $2T \cos \theta = mg$ we need mg and θ to find T. We need both XY and XZ to find θ, and so no piece of information can be omitted: **1**, **2** and **4** are needed for T, **3** is needed for the natural length; **3** and **4** are needed for the extension.

Thus the key is **E**.

Example 25 Find the volume generated when the region inside a closed curve lying in the $x-y$ plane is rotated through 2π radians about Ox.

1 The area of the region enclosed by the curve is given

2 The coordinates of the centroid of the area enclosed by the curve are given

3 The curve is not intersected by Ox

4 The curve is not intersected by Oy

As there is no information giving the equation of the curve, the problem can only be solved by using a theorem of Pappus. Students often remember that the volume of revolution is found by multiplying the area by the length of the path of the centroid without also remembering that this is only true for a closed curve which does not cut the axis about which it is rotating. Hence, **1** and **2** are needed to apply the formula and **3** is needed to satisfy the conditions. **4**, however, is not needed as the y-axis is not involved in any way. Hence the key is **D**. Incidentally, **2** provides more than is needed, as only the y-coordinate of the centroid is required.

As in the previous section, it may be necessary to look out for a special case which can be implicit in the data supplied.

Example 26 Find $|z_1 + z_2|$.

1 $\arg(z_1 + z_2) = \pi/3$

2 $|z_1| = 3$

3 $|z_2| = 2$

4 $|z_1 - z_2| = 5$

Looking at **2**, **3** and **4** we see that $|z_1| + |z_2| = |z_1 - z_2|$ and if this is interpreted by an Argand diagram it means that if P_1 and P_2 represent z_1 and z_2 respectively, then P_1OP_2 is a straight line and we can deduce that $|z_1 + z_2| = 1$, so that the problem is solved. The key, therefore, is **A**.

Sometimes the question asks you to prove a fact, and this type needs particular care as you must find enough information to prove the *truth* of the statement.

Example 27 Show that the curve $y = \dfrac{x-p}{(x-q)(x-r)}$ has three distinct asymptotes.

1 $p \neq 0$

2 $q \neq r$

3 $p \neq q$

4 $p \neq r$

Expressing y as $\dfrac{A}{x-q} + \dfrac{B}{x-r}$, we can see immediately that the asymptotes are $x = q$, $x = r$ and $y = 0$. This means that we need to look out for any facts given which would prevent the question being answered in this way or would not give three distinct asymptotes. Taking them in turn, **1** gives $p \neq 0$. But, if p were equal to 0, we should still be able to write the partial fractions as before, and so **1** is unnecessary and the key is **A**. In an examination you would then pass on to the next question. However, it is instructive to see why the others are necessary. (The examiner may not be so obliging as to give key **A**!) **2** is obviously necessary for distinct asymptotes and, if $p = q$ or $p = r$, we should get cancellation in the original fraction and so lose one of our asymptotes, so that **3** and **4** are necessary.

V Data sufficiency

In the previous section we were concerned with how much information was necessary in order to solve a problem. The remaining type of question, data sufficiency, asks how much is *sufficient* to solve a problem.

Example 28 Find a unique value for $\sin 2\theta$.

1 $\cos \theta = \frac{1}{2}$

2 $\tan \theta = \sqrt{3}$

Using the identity $\sin 2\theta \equiv 2\sin \theta \cos \theta$ we see that it is necessary to find $\sin \theta$. From either **1** or **2** we get $\sin \theta = \pm(\sqrt{3})/2$. It is only by taking both together that we see that θ is a first quadrant angle and so $\sin \theta = (\sqrt{3})/2$.

Hence the key is **D**.

Example 29 $P(X) = \frac{1}{3}$, $P(Y) = \frac{1}{4}$. Find $P(X \cup Y)$.

1 $P(X \cap Y) = \frac{1}{12}$

2 X and Y are independent

Using the result

$$P(X \cup Y) = P(X) + P(Y) - P(X \cap Y)$$

and having been given P(X) and P(Y), it is sufficient to be given P($X \cap Y$) in order to solve the problem. Hence, **1** is sufficient. However, **2** also is sufficient as the independence of X and Y gives us $P(X \cap Y) = P(X).P(Y)$. Hence, either **1** or **2** is sufficient and the key is **A**.

Example 30

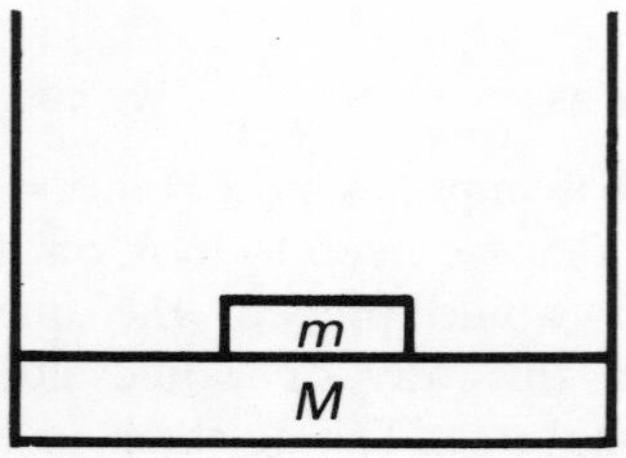

A load of mass m kg rests on a platform of mass M kg which descends with acceleration 2 m s^{-2}. Find the reaction between the load and the platform.

1 $m = 50$

2 $M = 100$

In order to solve the problem we need to consider the (downward) motion of the load, giving us the equation $mg - R = 2m$, where R newtons is the required reaction. To find R, we need m, so that **1** is sufficient. The other possibility would be to consider the motion of the platform, but, as we have no information about the tension in the supporting cables, we should not have sufficient information to solve the problem in this way. The key, then, is **B**.

In examples in which you are asked to prove a fact, it is important to make sure that *enough* information is given, not merely that the given information is consistent with the fact to be proved.

Example 31 Prove that a given system of coplanar forces is in equilibrium.

1 The sum of the resolved parts of the forces in a given direction is zero

2 The algebraic sum of the moments of the forces about each of two distinct points is zero

In this example, **1** and **2** together are not sufficient to ensure equilibrium. We can best see this by finding a case in which **1** and **2** are satisfied but the system is not in equilibrium. We are, in fact, finding a counter-example.

When a coplanar system of forces is not in equilibrium it can be reduced either to a single force or to a couple. **2** ensures that this system cannot be reduced to a couple. Could it then be reduced to a single force? If that force were in a direction perpendicular to that in **1**, this would be a possibility. If, moreover, the two distinct points were on its line of action, this would take care of **2**. Hence the system is not necessarily in equilibrium and the key is **E**.

Test 1

Time allowed: 1 hour

SECTION I

Questions 1–20 **(Twenty questions)**

1. $e^{\frac{1}{2}\ln x} =$

A $\ln(x^2)$

B $\ln(\sqrt{x})$

C x^2

D $\frac{1}{2}x$

E $\sqrt{x}$

2. $\frac{d}{dx}\left(\frac{x-1}{\sqrt{x}}\right) =$

A $2\sqrt{x}$

B $\frac{x+1}{x\sqrt{x}}$

C $\frac{3x-1}{2\sqrt{x}}$

D $\frac{x+1}{2x\sqrt{x}}$

E $\frac{3x-1}{2x\sqrt{x}}$

3. $\cos(\pi + \theta) \equiv$

A $-\cos\theta$

B $\cos\theta$

C $\sin\theta$

D $-\sin\theta$

E $-1 + \cos\theta$

4. The complete solution set of the inequality
$$x^2 + 2x - 15 < 0,$$
where $x \in \mathbb{R}$, is

A $\{x : x > -5\}$

B $\{x : -5 < x < 3\}$

C $\{x : x > 3\}$

D $\{x : -3 < x < 5\}$

E $\{x : x < -5\} \cup \{x : x > 3\}$

5. $\int \tan x \, dx =$

A $\ln\cos x$ + constant

B $\sec^2 x$ + constant

C $\ln\sec x$ + constant

D $\ln\operatorname{cosec} x$ + constant

E $\ln\sin x$ + constant

6. $\sum_{r=1}^{n} r^2 =$

A $n(n+1)/2$

B $n^2(n+1)^2/4$

C $n(n+1)(n+2)/3$

D $n(n+1)(2n+1)/3$

E $n(n+1)(2n+1)/6$

7. $z^2 + 1 \equiv$

A $(z + 1)(z - 1)$

B $(z + 1)^2$

C $(z + i)^2$

D $(z + i)(z - i)$

E none of the above

8. The first two terms in the binomial expansion of $\frac{1}{3x - 2}$, where $|x| < \frac{2}{3}$, in ascending powers of x are

A $-\frac{1}{2}, -\frac{3x}{4}$

B $-\frac{1}{2}, +\frac{3x}{4}$

C $\frac{1}{2}, -\frac{3x}{4}$

D $\frac{1}{3}, +\frac{2x}{9}$

E $\frac{1}{3x}, +\frac{2}{9x^2}$

9.

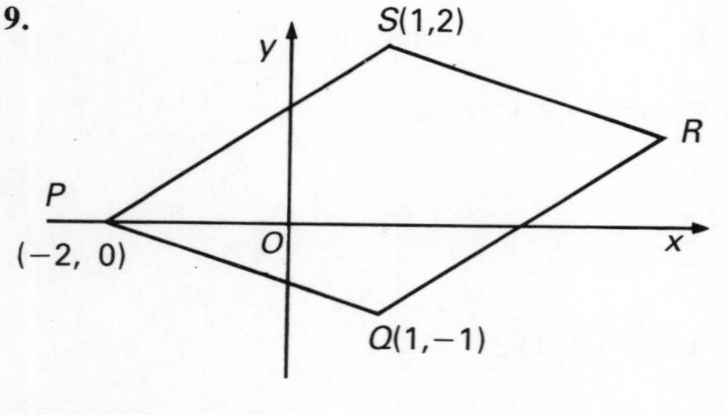

$PQRS$ is a parallelogram. The coordinates of R are

A (3, 1)

B (4, 1)

C (4, 2)

D (3, 2)

E (2, 1)

10. Given that $x = a$ is an approximation to a root of the equation $f(x) = 0$, then, in general, a closer approximation is given by

A $x = a + \frac{f(a)}{f'(a)}$

B $x = a + \frac{f'(a)}{f(a)}$

C $x = a - \frac{f(a)}{f'(a)}$

D $x = a - \frac{f'(a)}{f''(a)}$

E $x = a - \frac{f'(a)}{f(a)}$

11. $\mathbf{u} = 4\mathbf{i} - 3\mathbf{j}$, $\mathbf{v} = -6\mathbf{i} + 3\mathbf{j}$.
$\mathbf{u} \cdot \mathbf{v} =$

A $-2\mathbf{i}$

B $-24\mathbf{i} - 9\mathbf{j}$

C -3

D -33

E 30

12. Which one of the following can be seen, BY INSPECTION, NOT to be a factor of

$$6x^4 - 5x^3 - 53x^2 + 45x - 9\ ?$$

A $2x - 1$

B $x - 3$

C $x + 3$

D $3x - 1$

E $4x - 3$

13. $\dfrac{x + 7}{x^2 - x - 6} \equiv$

A $\dfrac{2}{x - 3} - \dfrac{1}{x + 2}$

B $\dfrac{2}{x + 2} - \dfrac{1}{x - 3}$

C $\dfrac{9}{5(x - 2)} - \dfrac{4}{5(x + 3)}$

D $\dfrac{4}{5(x - 2)} - \dfrac{9}{5(x + 3)}$

E $\dfrac{1}{x + 2} + \dfrac{2}{x - 3}$

14. Given that $\cos^2 x = \dfrac{16}{25}$, where $x \in \mathbb{R}$ and $\pi \leqslant x \leqslant 2\pi$, then the possible value(s) of $\sin x$ is (are)

A $\dfrac{3}{5}$ only

B $-\dfrac{3}{5}$ only

C $\pm\dfrac{3}{5}$

D $-\dfrac{3}{4}$ only

E $\pm\dfrac{3}{4}$

15. Given that $x = t^2$, $y = t^3$, then $\dfrac{dx}{dy} =$

A $\dfrac{1}{t}$

B $\dfrac{2}{3t}$

C $\dfrac{3t}{2}$

D $\dfrac{2t}{3}$

E $\dfrac{3}{2t}$

16. $\sin\theta + \sqrt{3}\cos\theta \equiv r\cos(\theta + \alpha)$, where $r > 0$ and $-\pi/2 \leqslant \alpha \leqslant \pi/2$.

A $r = 2,\quad \alpha = \pi/6$

B $r = 2,\quad \alpha = \pi/3$

C $r = 2,\quad \alpha = -\pi/3$

D $r = 2,\quad \alpha = -\pi/6$

E $r = 4,\quad \alpha = -\pi/6$

17.

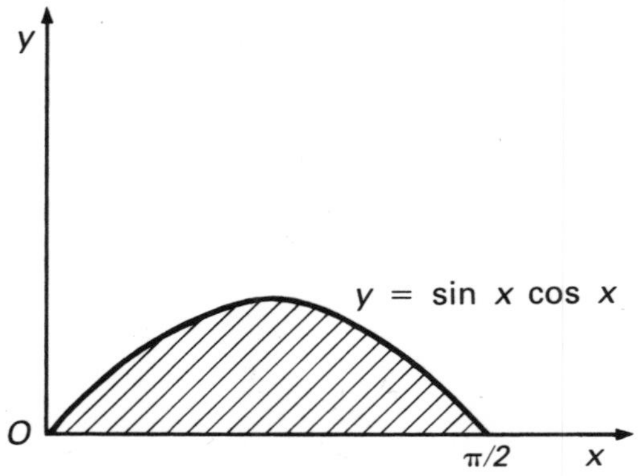

The area, in square units, of the shaded region is

A $\dfrac{1}{2}$

B $\dfrac{1}{4}$

C 1

D $\pi/2$

E $\dfrac{1}{8}$

18. The roots of the equation $x^2 - 4x + 7 = 0$ are α and β. An equation whose roots are α/β and β/α is

A $7x^2 - 2x - 7 = 0$

B $7x^2 + 2x + 7 = 0$

C $7x^2 - 2x + 7 = 0$

D $7x^2 - 30x + 7 = 0$

E none of the above

19. Which one of the following is an odd function of x?

A $f : x \mapsto |x|^3$

B $f : x \mapsto \sin^2 x$

C $f : x \mapsto (1 - x)^5$

D $f : x \mapsto e^{-x}$

E $f : x \mapsto -\sin 2x$

20. Given that

$$\lg(y + 2) + 2\lg x = 1,$$

then $y =$

A $\dfrac{1}{x^2} - 2$

B $\dfrac{5}{x} - 2$

C $\dfrac{10}{x^2} - 2$

D $\dfrac{1}{2x} - 2$

E $8 - x^2$

SECTION II

Questions 21–30 **(Ten Questions)**

21. Given that $\tan(x/2) = t$, then

1 $\cos x = \dfrac{1 - t^2}{1 + t^2}$

2 $\sin x = \dfrac{2t}{1 - t^2}$

3 $\dfrac{dx}{dt} = \dfrac{2}{1 - t^2}$

22. l is the line with equation $4x - 3y = 5$.

1 The gradient of l is $-4/3$

2 l touches the circle $x^2 + y^2 = 1$

3 The area of the finite region enclosed by l and the coordinate axes is 25/24 units^2

23. The circle $x^2 + y^2 + 2gx + 2fy + c = 0$ has centre $(-2, 4)$ and radius 6.

1 $g = -2$

2 $f = 4$

3 $c = -16$

24. $z = \dfrac{2 - i}{1 + 2i}$.

1 $|z| = 1$

2 $zz^* = 1$

3 $z + z^* = 0$

25. $f(x) \equiv x^3 + 3x - 5$.

1 The equation $f(x) = 0$ has just one real root

2 The equation $f(x) = 0$ has a root in the interval $[1, 2]$

3 The curve $y = f(x)$ has just one asymptote

26. p, q, r are 3 positive unequal integers in geometric progression.

1 $pr = q^2$

2 $\sqrt{(r/p)}$ is the common ratio of the progression

3 $\ln p$, $\ln q$ and $\ln r$ are numbers in arithmetic progression

27. $3^x = 1{\cdot}72$.

1 $x = \log_3 1{\cdot}72$

2 $5{\cdot}16 = 3^{1+x}$

3 $3{\cdot}44 = 3^{2x}$

28. Which of the following relations will give a straight line when $\dfrac{1}{x}$ is plotted against y?

1 $xy + 3x = 2$

2 $x + y = 2xy$

3 $\dfrac{2}{x} + y = 3x$

29. f and g are functions of x defined for $x \in \mathbb{R}$. It is necessarily true that

1 $f^{-1} = \dfrac{1}{f}$

2 $(fg)^{-1} = f^{-1}g^{-1}$

3 $ff^{-1}: x \mapsto x$

30. The plane $x - 2y - 4z = 3$

1 passes through the point $(-1, 1, -1)$

2 meets the x-axis at the point $(3, 0, 0)$

3 is perpendicular to the line $x = t - 2,\ y = 4 - 2t,\ z = 7 - 4t$

Test 2

Time allowed: 1 hour

SECTION I

Questions 1–20 **(Twenty questions)**

1. Given that $\frac{1}{4^{2x}} = 8^{10-x}$, then $x =$

A -30

B 30

C 20

D -20

E -10

2. Which one of the following is an even function of x?

A $f : x \mapsto \sin x$

B $f : x \mapsto \tan x$

C $f : x \mapsto (1 - x)^2$

D $f : x \mapsto -x^2$

E $f : x \mapsto \sin 2x$

3. $y = x(3 + x^2)^7$.

$\frac{dy}{dx} =$

A $14x(3 + x^2)^6$

B $14x^2(3 + x^2)^6$

C $(3 + 15x^2)(3 + x^2)^6$

D $(x^2 + 7x + 3)(3 + x^2)^6$

E $(x^2 + 14x + 3)(3 + x^2)^6$

4. Given that $\tan\theta = t$, then $\sin 2\theta =$

A $\frac{2t}{1 - t^2}$

B $\frac{1 - t^2}{1 + t^2}$

C $\frac{1 + t^2}{1 - t^2}$

D $\frac{2t}{t^2 - 1}$

E $\frac{2t}{1 + t^2}$

5. Given that $0 < \theta < \pi/2$, then the principal value of the argument of the complex number $\cos\theta - i\sin\theta$ is

A θ

B $-\theta$

C $\pi - \theta$

D $\pi + \theta$

E $\theta - \pi$

6. The coefficient of x^3 in the expansion in ascending powers of x of $(1 + x)^{1/2}$ is, for $|x| < 1$,

A $\frac{1}{16}$

B $-\frac{1}{16}$

C $\frac{5}{16}$

D $-\frac{5}{16}$

E $-\frac{1}{8}$

7. $\int_{-1}^{2} \frac{1}{3+2x}\,dx =$

A $\ln 7$

B $\frac{1}{2}\ln 7$

C $2\ln 7$

D $\frac{1}{2}\ln(7/5)$

E $2 - \frac{2}{7^2}$

8. The roots of a quadratic equation in x are α and β. The substitution $x = 2y + 3$ gives a quadratic equation in y whose roots are

A $(2\alpha + 3)$ and $(2\beta + 3)$

B $(2\alpha - 3)$ and $(2\beta - 3)$

C $\frac{1}{2}(\alpha - 3)$ and $\frac{1}{2}(\beta - 3)$

D $\frac{1}{2}(\alpha + 3)$ and $\frac{1}{2}(\beta + 3)$

E $(\alpha - 3)$ and $(\beta - 3)$

9. $\overrightarrow{OP} = 2\mathbf{i} - 2\mathbf{j} + \mathbf{k}$, $\overrightarrow{PQ} = 2\mathbf{i} + 2\mathbf{j} - \mathbf{k}$,

$|\overrightarrow{OQ}| =$

A $2\sqrt{5}$

B $3\sqrt{2}$

C 6

D 9

E 4

10. The complete set of values of x for which

$$x^2 + 5x + 6 > 0,$$

where $x \in \mathbb{R}$, is

A $\mathbb{R}$

B $\{x : x < 1\} \cup \{x : x > 6\}$

C $\{x : -2 < x < 3\}$

D $\{x : 1 < x < 6\}$

E $\{x : x < -3\} \cup \{x : x > -2\}$

11. The general solution of the differential equation

$$\frac{dy}{dx} = \frac{y}{x}$$

is, P being an arbitrary constant,

A $x^2 - y^2 = P$

B $y = Pe^x$

C $\frac{1}{x^2} - \frac{1}{y^2} = P$

D $y = Px$

E $xy = P$

12. $\sum_{r=0}^{\infty} \left(-\frac{2}{5}\right)^r =$

A $-\frac{5}{3}$

B $-\frac{5}{7}$

C $\frac{5}{7}$

D $\frac{5}{3}$

E $-\frac{2}{7}$

13. Given that $f : x \mapsto \ln(1 + x)$ for $x \in \mathbb{R}$, $x > -1$, then $f^{-1} : x \mapsto$

A $\frac{1}{\ln(1+x)}$

B $-\ln(1 + x)$

C $e^{(x-1)}$

D $e^x - 1$

E $e^{(1+x)}$

14.

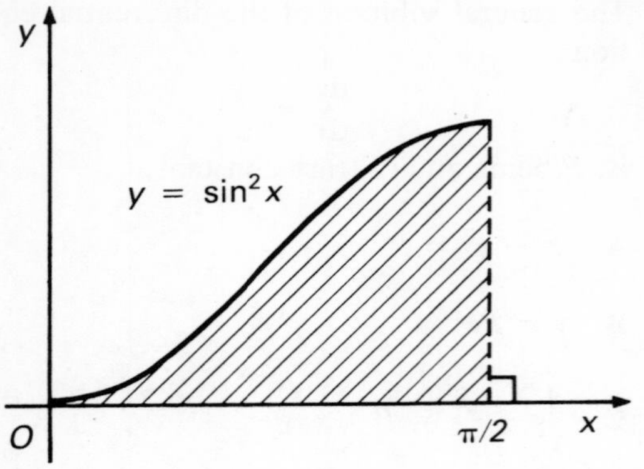

The area, in square units, of the shaded region is

A $\frac{\pi}{4}$

B $\frac{1}{2}$

C $\frac{\pi}{4} - \frac{1}{2}$

D 1

E $\frac{\pi}{2}$

15. The gradient of the tangent to the curve $y = (x - 2)/(x - 1)$ at the point where $x = 3$ is

A $-\frac{1}{4}$

B $\frac{1}{4}$

C $-\frac{3}{4}$

D $\frac{1}{2}$

E $\frac{3}{4}$

16. $\frac{\ln 40}{\ln 8} =$

A $\ln 5$

B $\ln 32$

C $\ln 40 - \ln 8$

D $1 + \ln\left(\frac{5}{8}\right)$

E none of the above

17. The number of roots, which lie in the range $0 \leqslant \theta \leqslant 2\pi$, of the equation $4 \sin \theta = \sin 2\theta$, is

A 0

B 2

C 3

D 4

E more than 4

18. Given that the expression $(x^3 + ax^2 + b)$ has factors $(x - 1)$ and $(x + 2)$, then

A $a = 7/3, \quad b = -4/3$

B $a = 4/3, \quad b = -7/3$

C $a = -7/3, \quad b = 4/3$

D $a = 3, \quad b = -4$

E $a = -3, \quad b = 4$

19. $z_1 = 2 - i$, $z_2 = 3 + 4i$.

$\left|\frac{z_2}{z_1}\right|^2 =$

A $\sqrt{5}$

B 5

C $\frac{125}{9}$

D $\left(\frac{2 + 11i}{5}\right)^2$

E $\left(\frac{10 + 5i}{5}\right)^2$

20. Which one of the following could be the graph of $\ln |x|$?

A

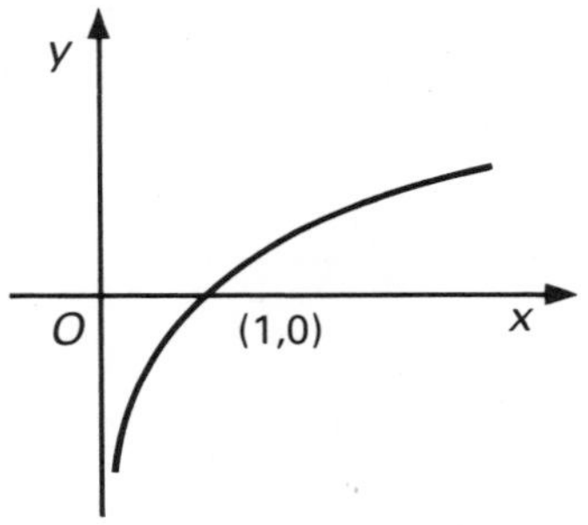

D

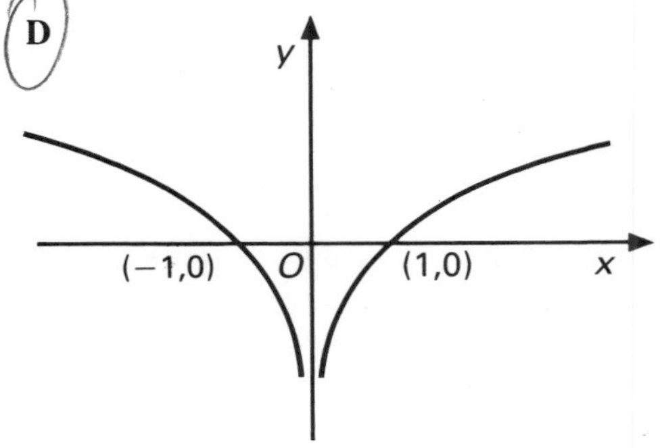

B

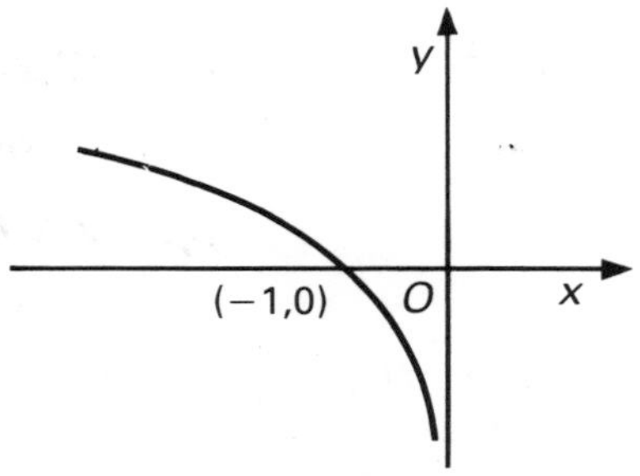

E

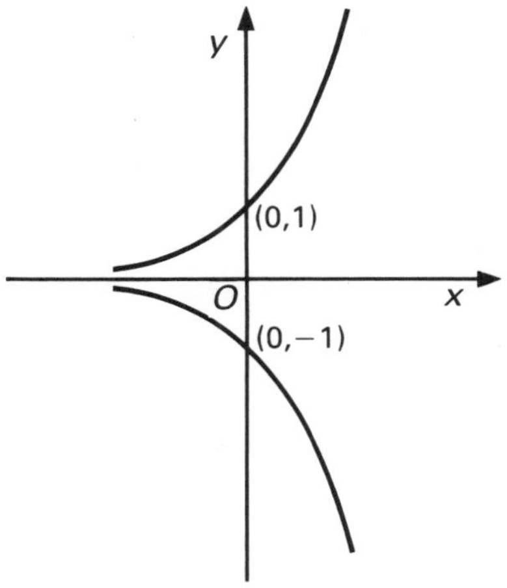

C

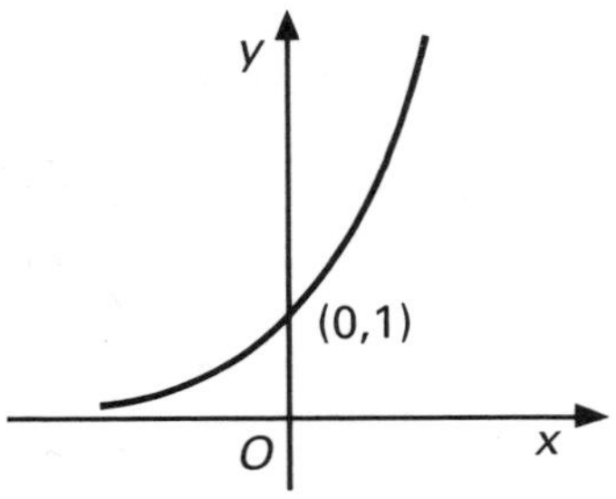

SECTION II

Questions 21–30 **(Ten questions)**

21. In an arithmetic series of 9 terms, the first term is 5 and the last term is 23.

1 The common difference is 2

2 The fifth term is 13

3 The sum of the series is 126

answer E

$a, a+d, a+2d, a+3d, a+4d, a+5d, a+6d, a+7d, a+8d$

$5, 5+d, 5+2d, 5+3d, 5+4d, 5+5d, 5+6d, 5+7d, 5+8d$

$5+8d = 23$, $8d = 18$, $d = \frac{18}{8} = \frac{9}{4}$

fifth term $= 5+4d = 5+4\cdot\frac{9}{4} = 14$

$S_9 = \frac{9}{2}(5+23) = 126$

22. $$\frac{1}{(x+1)(x+2)(x+3)} \equiv \frac{P}{x+1} + \frac{Q}{x+2} + \frac{R}{x+3}.$$

1 $P = \frac{1}{2}$

2 $Q = -1$

3 $R = \frac{1}{6}$

$\Rightarrow 1 = P(x+2)(x+3) + Q(x+1)(x+3) + R(x+1)(x+2)$

let $x = -1 \Rightarrow 1 = 2P \Rightarrow P = \frac{1}{2}$

let $x = -2 \Rightarrow 1 = -Q \Rightarrow Q = -1$

let $x = -3 \Rightarrow 1 = 2R \Rightarrow R = \frac{1}{2}$

answer B

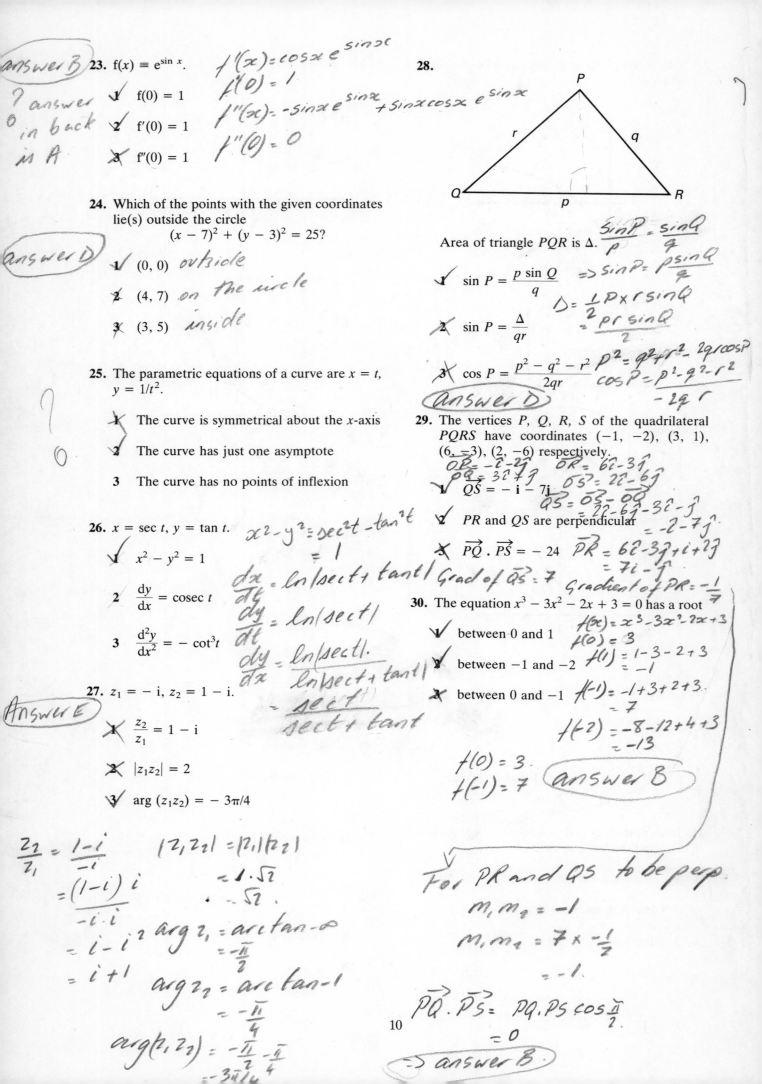

23. $f(x) \equiv e^{\sin x}$.

$f'(x) = \cos x \, e^{\sin x}$
$f'(0) = 1$

✓ $f(0) = 1$

✓ $f'(0) = 1$

✗ $f''(0) = 1$

$f''(x) = -\sin x \, e^{\sin x} + \sin x \cos x \, e^{\sin x}$
$f''(0) = 0$

24. Which of the points with the given coordinates lie(s) outside the circle
$$(x - 7)^2 + (y - 3)^2 = 25?$$

✓ (0, 0) *outside*

✗ (4, 7) *on the circle*

✗ (3, 5) *inside*

25. The parametric equations of a curve are $x = t$, $y = 1/t^2$.

✗ The curve is symmetrical about the x-axis

✗ The curve has just one asymptote

3   The curve has no points of inflexion

26. $x = \sec t$, $y = \tan t$.

$x^2 - y^2 = \sec^2 t - \tan^2 t$
$= 1$

✓ $x^2 - y^2 = 1$

2    $\dfrac{dy}{dx} = \operatorname{cosec} t$

3    $\dfrac{d^2y}{dx^2} = -\cot^3 t$

$\dfrac{dx}{dt} = \ln|\sec t + \tan t|$

$\dfrac{dy}{dt} = \ln|\sec t|$

$\dfrac{dy}{dx} = \dfrac{\ln|\sec t|}{\ln|\sec t + \tan t|}$

$= \dfrac{\sec t}{\sec t + \tan t}$

27. $z_1 = -i$, $z_2 = 1 - i$.

✗ $\dfrac{z_2}{z_1} = 1 - i$

✗ $|z_1 z_2| = 2$

✓ $\arg(z_1 z_2) = -3\pi/4$

$\dfrac{z_2}{z_1} = \dfrac{1-i}{-i}$

$= \dfrac{(1-i)\,i}{-i \cdot i}$

$= i - i^2$

$= i + 1$

$|z_1 z_2| = |z_1||z_2|$
$= 1 \cdot \sqrt{2}$
$= \sqrt{2}$

$\arg z_1 = \arctan{-\infty}$
$= -\dfrac{\pi}{2}$

$\arg z_2 = \arctan{-1}$
$= -\dfrac{\pi}{4}$

$\arg(z_1 z_2) = -\dfrac{\pi}{2} - \dfrac{\pi}{4}$
$= -3\pi/4$

28.

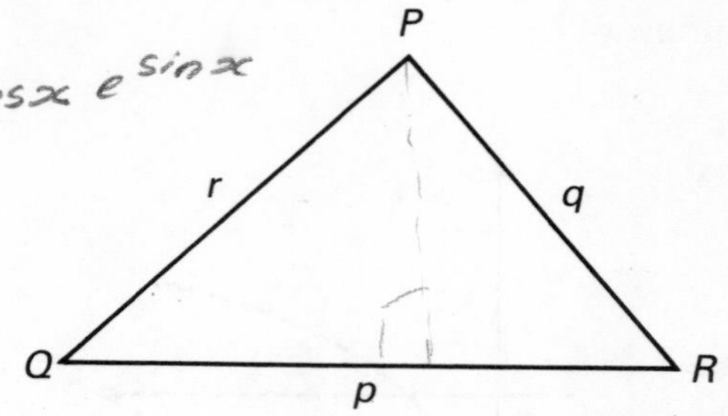

Area of triangle PQR is Δ.

$\dfrac{\sin P}{p} = \dfrac{\sin Q}{q}$

✓ $\sin P = \dfrac{p \sin Q}{q}$ $\Rightarrow \sin P = \dfrac{p \sin Q}{q}$

✗ $\sin P = \dfrac{\Delta}{qr}$

$\Delta = \dfrac{1}{2} p \times r \sin Q$
$= \dfrac{pr \sin Q}{2}$

✗ $\cos P = \dfrac{p^2 - q^2 - r^2}{2qr}$

$p^2 = q^2 + r^2 - 2qr\cos P$
$\cos P = \dfrac{p^2 - q^2 - r^2}{-2qr}$

29. The vertices P, Q, R, S of the quadrilateral $PQRS$ have coordinates $(-1, -2)$, $(3, 1)$, $(6, -3)$, $(2, -6)$ respectively.

$\overrightarrow{OP} = -i - 2j$ $\overrightarrow{OR} = 6i - 3j$
$\overrightarrow{OQ} = 3i + j$ $\overrightarrow{OS} = 2i - 6j$

✓ $\overrightarrow{QS} = -i - 7j$

$\overrightarrow{QS} = \overrightarrow{OS} - \overrightarrow{OQ}$
$= 2i - 6j - 3i - j$
$= -i - 7j$

✓ PR and QS are perpendicular

✗ $\overrightarrow{PQ} \cdot \overrightarrow{PS} = -24$

$\overrightarrow{PR} = 6i - 3j + i + 2j$
$= 7i - j$

Grad of $\overrightarrow{QS} = 7$

Gradient of $PR = -\dfrac{1}{7}$

30. The equation $x^3 - 3x^2 - 2x + 3 = 0$ has a root

✓ between 0 and 1

✓ between -1 and -2

✗ between 0 and -1

$f(x) = x^3 - 3x^2 - 2x + 3$
$f(0) = 3$
$f(1) = 1 - 3 - 2 + 3$
$= -1$
$f(-1) = -1 + 3 + 2 + 3$
$= 7$
$f(-2) = -8 - 12 + 4 + 3$
$= -13$

$f(0) = 3.$
$f(-1) = 7$

For PR and QS to be perp.

$m_1 m_2 = -1$
$m_1 m_2 = 7 \times -\dfrac{1}{7}$
$= -1.$

$\overrightarrow{PQ} \cdot \overrightarrow{PS} = PQ \cdot PS \cos\dfrac{\pi}{2}$
$= 0$

$\Rightarrow$ answer B

TEST 3

Time allowed: 1 hour

SECTION I

Questions 1–20 **(Twenty Questions)**

1. $\frac{d}{dx}(e^{\cos x}) =$

A $e^{\cos x}$

B $e^{\cos x} \sin x$

C $-e^{\cos x} \sin x$

D $e^{\sin x}$

E $e^{\sin x} \cos x$

2. The gradient of the straight line with equation $ax + by = c$, where a and b are non zero, is

A a/b

B $-a/b$

C b/a

D $-b/a$

E c

3. $\sum_{r=1}^{n} (2r - 1) =$

A n^2

B $n^2 - 1$

C $n^2 + n - 1$

D $n^2 + 2n$

E $n^2 + n$

4. The number of arrangements which can be made using all the letters of the word RAPIDS, if the vowels are never separated, is

A 30

B 60

C 120

D 240

E 720

5. $\int \frac{1 + 3x^2}{x} dx =$

A $\frac{x + x^3}{x}$ + constant

B $-\frac{1}{x^2} + 3$ + constant

C $x^3 + \ln x$ + constant

D $3 + \ln x$ + constant

E $\frac{3}{2}x^2 + \ln x$ + constant

6. The principal value of the argument of the complex number $-1 - i\sqrt{3}$ is

A $-\frac{2\pi}{3}$

B $-\frac{5\pi}{6}$

C $\frac{2\pi}{3}$

D $\frac{5\pi}{6}$

E $-\frac{\pi}{3}$

7. The complete solution set of the inequality

$$x^2 + 4x + 5 > 0,$$

where $x \in \mathbb{R}$, is

A $\mathbb{R}^+$

B $\{x : x > 5\}$

C $\{x : -1 < x < 5\}$

D $\{x : x > 5\} \cup \{x : x < -1\}$

E $\mathbb{R}$

8. $\dfrac{dy}{dx} + y \cos x = 0$ and $y = 1$ when $x = \pi/2$. Then $y =$

A $e^{(1+\cos x)}$

B $e^{(1-\sin x)}$

C $e^{(-1+\sin x)}$

D $e^{(1-\cos x)}$

E $e^{-\sin x}$

9. $\cos^2\theta + 3\sin^2\theta \equiv$

A $2 + \cos 2\theta$

B $3 - 2\cos 2\theta$

C $2 - \cos 2\theta$

D $2\cos 2\theta - 1$

E none of the above

10. Which one of the following functions is odd and of period 2?

A $\sin(\pi x/2)$

B $\sin(\pi x)$

C $\cos(\pi x)$

D $x \sin(\pi x)$

E $\sin(\pi x) + \cos(\pi x)$

11. The arithmetic mean of α and β is 4·5 and their geometric mean is 2. A quadratic equation whose roots are α and β is

A $2x^2 - 9x + 4 = 0$

B $x^2 + 9x + 4 = 0$

C $2x^2 + 9x + 4 = 0$

D $x^2 - 9x + 4 = 0$

E $x^2 + 9x - 4 = 0$

12. $\cos^{-1}\left(-\dfrac{\sqrt{3}}{2}\right) - \sin^{-1}\left(-\dfrac{\sqrt{3}}{2}\right) =$

A $-5\pi/6$

B $-\pi/2$

C $-\pi/6$

D $\pi/2$

E $7\pi/6$

13. The tangent of the acute angle between the lines $3x - y + 4 = 0$ and $x - 2y + 5 = 0$ is

A 1

B $\dfrac{7}{5}$

C -1

D 5

E -7

14. Given that the real root of the equation

$$x^3 - 6x^2 + 15x - 13 = 0$$

lies in the interval $[n, n + 1]$ where $n \in \mathbb{Z}$, then $n =$

A -2

B -1

C 0

D 1

E 2

15. Given that
$\ln x = p$, $\ln y = q$, $\ln z = r$,
where $x, y, z \in \mathbb{R}^+$, then

$\ln\left(\frac{x^a y^b}{z^c}\right) \equiv$

A $\frac{ap + bq}{cr}$

B $p^a + q^b - r^c$

C $\frac{abpq}{cr}$

D $\frac{p^a q^b}{c^r}$

E $ap + bq - cr$

16. The value(s) of p for which the vectors ($p\mathbf{i} + 2\mathbf{j} - 3p\mathbf{k}$) and ($p\mathbf{i} + \mathbf{k}$) are perpendicular is (are)

A 0 only

B 3 only

C 0 and 3

D 1 and 2

E 1 only

17. $y = \sin^{-1}(3x)$.

$\frac{dy}{dx} =$

A $-\frac{3\cos(3x)}{\sin^2(3x)}$

B $3\cos^{-1}(3x)$

C $\frac{1}{\sqrt{(1 - 9x^2)}}$

D $\frac{3}{\sqrt{(1 - 9x^2)}}$

E $\frac{1}{3\sqrt{(1 - 9x^2)}}$

18. The point P in the Argand diagram represents the complex number $4 + 3i$. The tangent of the angle made by OP with the imaginary axis is

A $\frac{3}{4}$

B $\frac{4}{3}$

C $\frac{3}{5}$

D $\frac{4}{5}$

E $\frac{5}{4}$

19. Given that
$$x^3 - ax^2 + bx - c \equiv (x - 1)^2(x + 1),$$
then

A $a = 1, \quad b = -1, \quad c = -1$

B $a = -1, \quad b = 1, \quad c = 1$

C $a = 1, \quad b = -1, \quad c = 1$

D $a = 3, \quad b = 3, \quad c = 1$

E none of the above

20. The general solution of the differential equation

$$\frac{dy}{dx} \cdot \cos x = y \sin x$$

is, P being an arbitrary constant,

A $y \cos x = P$

B $y \sec x = P$

C $y \sin x = P$

D $y = P \cos x$

E $y = P\,e^{\sec^2 x}$

SECTION II

Questions 21–30 **(Ten questions)**

21. z and z^* are conjugate complex numbers.

1 In the Argand diagram z^* is the reflection of z in the real axis

2 $(z_1 + z_2)^* = z_1^* + z_2^*$

3 $(z_1 - iz_2)^* = z_1^* + i\, z_2^*$

22. $f(x) \equiv x^2 + 2x + 5, \; x \in \mathbb{R}$.

1 $f(x) > 0$

2 The line $y = 4$ is a tangent to the curve $y = f(x)$

3 The maximum value of $f(x)$ is 4

23. The straight line

$$\mathbf{r} = (3\mathbf{i} - \mathbf{j} + 2\mathbf{k}) + t(5\mathbf{i} + 2\mathbf{j} - 4\mathbf{k}),$$

where t is a parameter,

1 passes through the point with position vector $(-2\mathbf{i} - 3\mathbf{j} + 6\mathbf{k})$

2 is parallel to the vector $(3\mathbf{i} - \mathbf{j} + 2\mathbf{k})$

3 is perpendicular to the vector $(\mathbf{i} - \mathbf{j} - 2\mathbf{k})$

24. Given that

$$\frac{3x^2 - x}{(x + 1)(x^2 + 3)} \equiv \frac{P}{x + 1} + \frac{Qx + R}{x^2 + 3}$$

where P, Q, R are constants, then

1 $P = -1$

2 $Q = 2$

3 $R = -3$

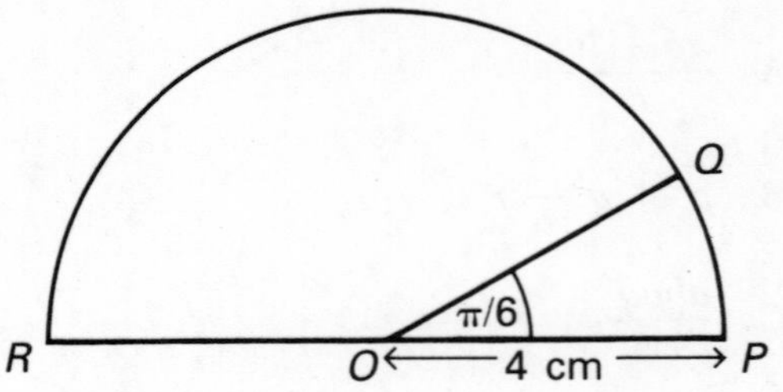

25. P, Q and R lie on the semi-circle with centre O and radius 4 cm.

1 The ratio of the lengths of the arcs PQ and QR is 1 : 5

2 The area of the triangle OPQ is 4 cm^2

3 The area of the sector OPQ is $8\pi/3$ cm^2

26. $f : x \mapsto 5 - 2x, \quad g : x \mapsto x^2/2, \quad x \in \mathbb{R}$.

1 $f^{-1} : x \mapsto \dfrac{1}{5 - 2x}, \quad x \in \mathbb{R}, \; x \neq 5/2$

2 $fg : x \mapsto (5 - 2x)^2/2, \quad x \in \mathbb{R}$

3 $ff : x \mapsto 4x - 5, \quad x \in \mathbb{R}$

27. The equation $x^3 - 5x^2 + 7x - 2 = 0$

1 has a root 2

2 has a root lying in the interval (0, 1)

3 has a root lying in the interval (−1, 0)

28. Given that $y = ax^n$, where a, n are positive constants and $n \neq 1$, then a straight line graph is obtained by plotting

1 $\log y$ against $\log x$

2 $\log (y/x)$ against $\log x$

3 y against x^n

29. $f(x) = f(2a - x)$, where a is a positive constant.

1 $f(x)$ is a periodic function

2 $f(x)$ is an even function

3 $\int_0^{2a} f(x)dx = 2\int_0^{a} f(x)dx$

30. The curve $y = x/(x + 2)$ has

1 only one asymptote

2 no stationary points

3 no inflexions

Test 4

Time allowed: 1 hour

SECTION I

Questions 1–20 **(Twenty questions)**

1. $p^x q^{2x} = r^3$, where $p, q, r \in \mathbb{R}^+$.
$x =$

A $\dfrac{3 \ln r}{\ln p + 2 \ln q}$

B $\dfrac{\ln r}{\ln p + \ln q}$

C $\dfrac{1}{3}(3 \ln r - \ln p - 2 \ln q)$

D $\dfrac{3 \ln r}{2 \ln (pq)}$

E $\dfrac{r}{(pq^2)^{1/3}}$

2. $z = \dfrac{3 - 2\text{i}}{2 - 3\text{i}}$.
$|z^*| =$

A 13

B $\sqrt{13}$

C $\dfrac{2}{3}$

D $\dfrac{3}{2}$

E 1

3. The first 3 terms of the expansion of $(1 - 2x)^{-1/2}$ in ascending powers of x are

A $1, +x, \quad -\frac{3}{2}x^2$

B $1, -x, \quad -\frac{1}{2}x^2$

C $1, +x, \quad -\frac{1}{2}x^2$

D $1, +x, \quad +\frac{3}{2}x^2$

E $1, -x, \quad +\frac{3}{2}x^2$

4. Given that α and β are the roots of the equation

$$px^2 + qx + r = 0,$$

where $pqr \neq 0$, then

$\dfrac{1}{\alpha^2\beta} + \dfrac{1}{\alpha\beta^2} =$

A $\dfrac{pq}{r^2}$

B $-\dfrac{pq}{r^2}$

C $\dfrac{q^2 - 2pr}{r^2}$

D $\dfrac{q^2 + 2pr}{r^2}$

E $-\dfrac{q}{r}$

5. Given that $\text{f}(x) = \text{e}^{x^3}$, $x \in \mathbb{R}^+$, then
$\text{f}^{-1}(x) =$

A e^{-x^3}

B e^{1/x^3}

C $(\ln x)^{1/3}$

D $\dfrac{1}{3} \ln x$

E $\ln(x^{1/3})$

6. $y = x^2 \cos x$.
$\dfrac{\text{d}y}{\text{d}x} =$

A $2x \cos x$

B $-x^2 \sin x$

C $x^2 \cos x - 2x \sin x$

D $2x \cos x + x^2 \sin x$

E $2x \cos x - x^2 \sin x$

7.

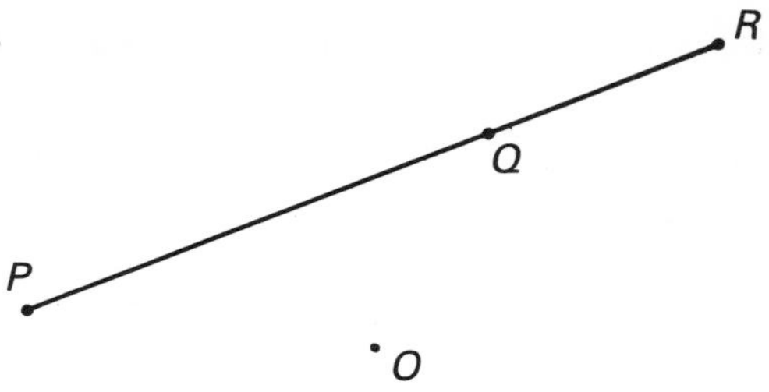

PQR is a straight line and $PQ = 2QR$.
$\overrightarrow{OQ} = 3\mathbf{i} - 2\mathbf{j}$, $\overrightarrow{OR} = \mathbf{i} + 3\mathbf{j}$.
$\overrightarrow{OP} =$

A $-\mathbf{i} + 8\mathbf{j}$

B $7\mathbf{i} - 12\mathbf{j}$

C $4\mathbf{i} - 10\mathbf{j}$

D $-4\mathbf{i} + 10\mathbf{j}$

E $-7\mathbf{i} + 12\mathbf{j}$

8. $\displaystyle\int \frac{1}{\sqrt{(9 - 4x^2)}}\, dx =$

A $\frac{1}{3}\sin^{-1}\left(\frac{3x}{2}\right)$ + constant

B $\frac{1}{3}\sin^{-1}\left(\frac{2x}{3}\right)$ + constant

C $\frac{1}{2}\sin^{-1}\left(\frac{3x}{2}\right)$ + constant

D $\frac{1}{2}\sin^{-1}\left(\frac{2x}{3}\right)$ + constant

E $\sin^{-1}\left(\frac{2x}{3}\right)$ + constant

9. The point $(-1, 3)$ is at one end of a diameter of the circle whose equation is

$$(x - 3)^2 + y^2 = 25.$$

The coordinates of the other end of this diameter are

A $(7, -3)$

B $(7, 3)$

C $(9, 3)$

D $(6, -3)$

E $(1, -3)$

10. The complete set of values of x for which

$$15x^2 \leqslant 12 - 11x,$$

where $x \in \mathbb{R}$, is

A $\{x : x \leqslant -\frac{4}{3}\} \cup \{x : x \geqslant \frac{3}{5}\}$

B $\{x : x \leqslant -\frac{3}{5}\} \cup \{x : x \geqslant \frac{4}{3}\}$

C $\{x : -\frac{4}{3} \leqslant x \leqslant \frac{3}{5}\}$

D $\{x : -\frac{3}{5} \leqslant x \leqslant \frac{4}{3}\}$

E $\{x : \frac{3}{5} \leqslant x \leqslant \frac{4}{3}\}$

11. The lengths of the sides of a triangle are in the ratios 6 : 5 : 4. Then the cosine of the largest angle of the triangle is

A $-\frac{3}{4}$

B $-\frac{1}{8}$

C $\frac{1}{8}$

D $\frac{9}{16}$

E $\frac{3}{4}$

12. Given that 3 is an approximation to the real root of the equation $f(x) = 0$, where

$$f(x) \equiv x^3 - x^2 - 19,$$

the next approximation obtained by the Newton–Raphson process is

A $2\frac{8}{9}$

B $3\frac{1}{9}$

C $3\frac{1}{10}$

D $2\frac{9}{10}$

E none of the above

13. $\frac{i^{47}}{i^{29}} =$

A -1

B 1

C $-i$

D i

E i^{-1}

14. Given that $(x + 1)$ and $(x - 2)$ are both factors of $(x^3 + ax^2 - 5x + b)$, where a and b are constants, then

A $a = -1, \quad b = 5$

B $a = 1, \quad b = -5$

C $a = -2, \quad b = 10$

D $a = 2, \quad b = -6$

E $a = -2, \quad b = 6$

15. The sum to infinity of the geometric series

$$\frac{1}{3} - \left(\frac{1}{3}\right)^3 + \left(\frac{1}{3}\right)^5 - \ldots$$

is

A $\frac{3}{10}$

B $\frac{3}{8}$

C $\frac{1}{2}$

D $\frac{9}{10}$

E $\frac{1}{4}$

16. Which one of the following curves does *not* have a point of inflexion at $x = 0$?

A $y = \sin x$

B $y = \tan x$

C $y = x^4$

D $y = x^3$

E $y = x^3 - x$

17. A solution of the differential equation

$$\frac{dy}{dx} = 2xy + 2x$$

is

A e^{x^2}

B $e^{x^2} - 1$

C $e^{x^2} + 1$

D $2e^{x^2} + 2$

E xe^{x^2}

18.

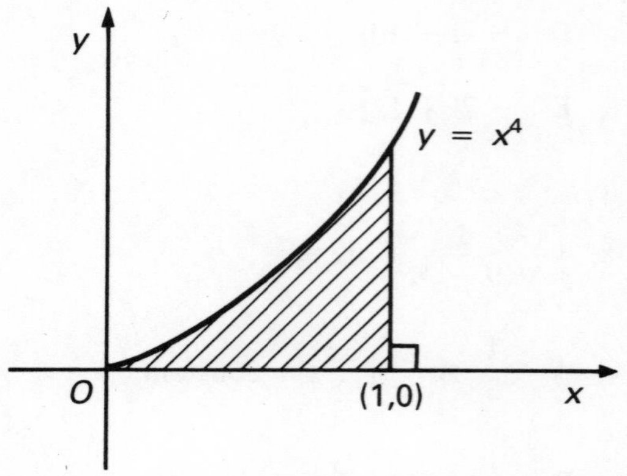

The volume, in cubic units, of the solid generated when the shaded region is rotated completely about Oy is

A $\pi/9$

B $\pi/3$

C $2\pi/3$

D $\pi/15$

E $8\pi/9$

19. $2 \cos 2\theta \cos 4\theta \equiv$

A $\cos 2\theta - \cos 6\theta$

B $\cos 2\theta + \cos 6\theta$

C $\cos 6\theta - \cos 2\theta$

D $\sin 6\theta - \sin 2\theta$

E $\sin 6\theta + \sin 2\theta$

20.

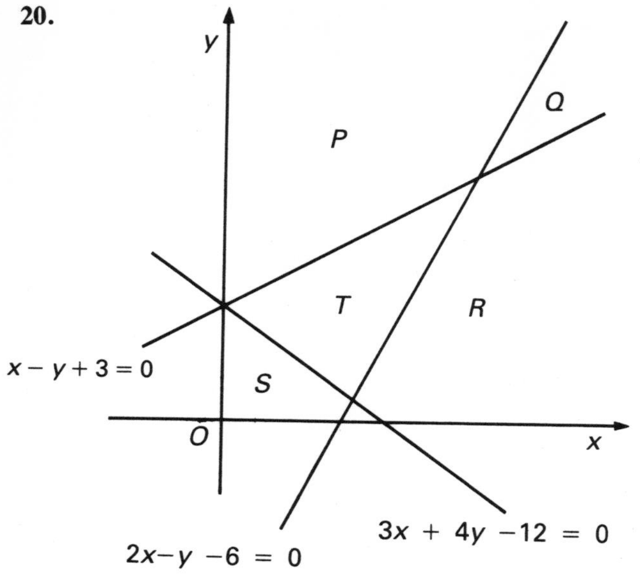

In which one of the labelled regions does the point with coordinates (4, 3) lie?

A P

B Q

C R

D S

E T

SECTION II

Questions 21–30 **(Ten questions)**

21. The curve $y = x^3 - 3x + 1$

1 has one maximum point and one minimum point

2 cuts the x-axis in 3 distinct points

3 has no point of inflexion

22. u and v are functions of x.

1 $\frac{d}{dx}(uv) = u\frac{dv}{dx} + v\frac{du}{dx}$

2 $\frac{d}{dx}\left(\frac{u}{v}\right) = \frac{u\frac{dv}{dx} - v\frac{du}{dx}}{v^2}$

3 $\int uv\, dx = u\int v\, dx - \int v\frac{du}{dx}\, dx$

23. $I_C = \int_0^{\pi/2} \cos^2 x\, dx, \quad I_S = \int_0^{\pi/2} \sin^2 x\, dx.$

1 $I_C = I_S$

2 $I_C + I_S = \frac{\pi}{2}$

3 $\int_0^{\pi} \sin^2 x\, dx = 2I_C$

24. $f(x) \equiv \frac{(x + 3)(x - 2)}{(x + 4)}$.

1 $f(x) \equiv x - 3 + \frac{6}{x + 4}$

2 $f(x) < 0$ when $-3 < x < 2$

3 The equation $f(x) = 0$ has roots $-4, -3$ and 2

25. $z = (\cos\theta + i\sin\theta)/(\cos\phi - i\sin\phi)$, where $0 < \theta < \pi/4$, $0 < \phi < \pi/4$.

1 $\arg z = (\theta - \phi)$

2 $\operatorname{Im} z = \sin(\theta - \phi)$

3 $|z| = 1$

26. The curve represented by the parametric equations
$x = \dfrac{a}{t}$, $y = at^2$, where $a > 0$,

1 is a parabola

2 is symmetrical about Oy

3 has an asymptote $y = 0$

27. The sum of the first n terms of a sequence is $n/(n^2 + 1)$.

1 The first term is $\frac{1}{2}$

2 As n tends to infinity, the nth term of the sequence tends to zero

3 All the terms after the first are negative

28. $\sin\alpha = \dfrac{1}{2}$, $\sin 2\alpha = -\dfrac{\sqrt{3}}{2}$.

1 $\cos\alpha = \dfrac{\sqrt{3}}{2}$

2 $\cos 2\alpha = \dfrac{1}{2}$

3 $\cos 4\alpha = -\dfrac{1}{2}$

29.

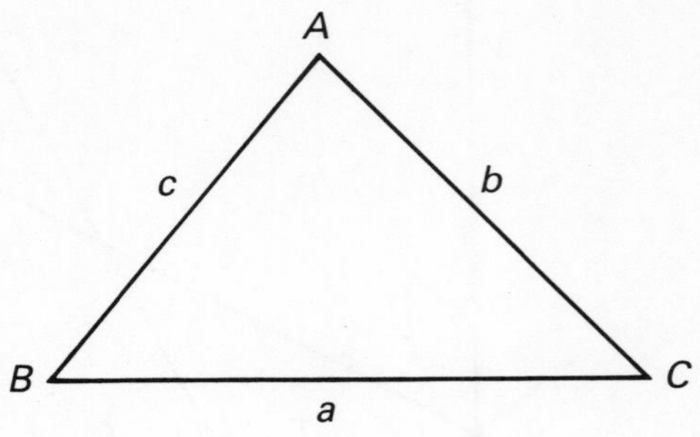

For the triangle ABC,

1 $a^2 + c^2 - b^2 = 2ac\cos B$

2 the area of the triangle is $\frac{1}{2}bc\cos A$

3 $a\sin A = b\sin B$

30. Given that $x, y \in \mathbb{R}$ and $x > y$, which of the following inequalities must necessarily be true?

1 $x^2 > y^2$

2 $\dfrac{1}{x} < \dfrac{1}{y}$

3 $x^3 > y^3$

TEST 5

Time allowed: 1 hour

SECTION I

Questions 1–20 **(Twenty questions)**

1. The period of the function f, where

$$f : x \mapsto 2 \sin\left(\frac{x}{3} - \frac{\pi}{2}\right), \quad x \in \mathbb{R},$$

is

A π

B $\pi/3$

C 3π

D 6π

E $11\pi/2$

2. The unit vector in the direction of $(\mathbf{a} - \mathbf{b})$, where

$$\mathbf{a} = (3\mathbf{i} - 5\mathbf{j} - 2\mathbf{k}),\ \mathbf{b} = (2\mathbf{i} - 3\mathbf{j} - 4\mathbf{k}),$$

is

A $\mathbf{i} - 2\mathbf{j} + 2\mathbf{k}$

B $\frac{1}{\sqrt{65}}(5\mathbf{i} - 2\mathbf{j} - 6\mathbf{k})$

C $\frac{1}{3}(\mathbf{i} - 2\mathbf{j} + 2\mathbf{k})$

D $\frac{1}{9}(\mathbf{i} - 2\mathbf{j} + 2\mathbf{k})$

E $\frac{1}{3}(-\mathbf{i} + 2\mathbf{j} - 2\mathbf{k})$

3. Given that $x = t - \sin t$, $y = 1 - \cos t$, then

$$\frac{dy}{dx} =$$

A $\tan(t/2)$

B $\cot(t/2)$

C $-\cot(t/2)$

D $\dfrac{1 - \sin t}{1 - \cos t}$

E $-\tan(t/2)$

4. The complete set of the real values of k for which the equation

$$x^2 + kx + 2k = 0$$

has real distinct roots is

A $\{k : k > 8\}$

B $\{k : k < 0\}$

C $\{k : 0 \leqslant k \leqslant 8\}$

D $\{k : k \leqslant 0\} \cup \{k : k \geqslant 8\}$

E $\{k : k < 0\} \cup \{k : k > 8\}$

5. $\displaystyle\int_{-1/2}^{1/2} \frac{1}{(1 - x)^2}\, dx =$

A $\dfrac{4}{3}$

B $-\dfrac{4}{3}$

C 1

D $\ln 3$

E $-\ln 3$

6. The gradient of that diameter of the circle

$$x^2 + y^2 + 6x - 8y = 0$$

which is perpendicular to the line joining the centre of the circle to the origin is

A $-\dfrac{4}{3}$

B $-\dfrac{3}{4}$

C $\dfrac{4}{3}$

D $-\dfrac{5}{4}$

E $\dfrac{3}{4}$

7. Given that

$$f : x \mapsto 2x,$$
$$g : x \mapsto 3x - 4,$$

for $x \in \mathbb{R}$, then
$f^{-1}g^{-1} : x \mapsto$

A $\dfrac{1}{2x(3x - 4)}$

B $\dfrac{x + 4}{6}$

C $\dfrac{x + 8}{6}$

D $\dfrac{1}{6x - 8}$

E $\dfrac{3x - 4}{2}$

8.

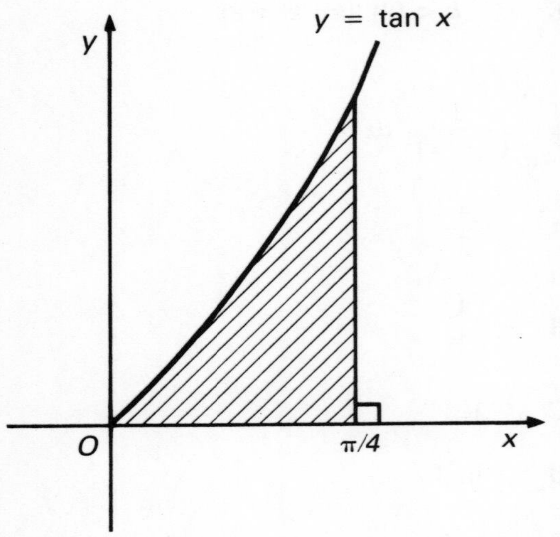

The area, in square units, of the shaded region is

A 1

B ln 2

C − ln 2

D $\frac{1}{2}$ ln 2

E − $\frac{1}{2}$ ln 2

9. Given that $x \in \mathbb{R}$, $y \in \mathbb{R}$,

$$e^y \frac{dy}{dx} = e^{-x}$$

and $y = 0$ when $x = 0$, then, when $x = -1$,

A $y = 1$

B $y = -\ln(e - 2)$

C $y = -1$

D $y = 1 + \ln 2$

E y cannot be found

10. Given that

$$\frac{1 + i}{x} = \frac{i}{y + i},$$

where x, $y \in \mathbb{R}$, then

A $x = 0, \quad y = 1$

B $x = 0, \quad y = -1$

C $x = 2, \quad y = 1$

D $x = -2, \quad y = 1$

E there is insufficient information for x and y to be found.

11. The number of ways in which n books can be chosen from $(m + n)$ different books is

A $\dfrac{(m + n)!}{n!}$

B $(m + n)! - m!$

C $(m + n)! - n!$

D $\dfrac{(m + n)!}{m!}$

E $\dfrac{(m + n)!}{m!n!}$

12. The coefficient of x^2 in the binomial expansion of $(1 - x)^5$ is

A -15

B -10

C $+10$

D $+15$

E $+20$

13. $\sum_{r=1}^{\infty} e^{-r}$

A $= \frac{1}{e - 1}$

B $= \frac{e}{e - 1}$

C $= \frac{1}{e + 1}$

D $= \frac{e}{e + 1}$

E does not converge

14. The roots of the equation $2x^2 + 7x + 3 = 0$ are α and β. An equation whose roots are $2\alpha + \beta$ and $\alpha + 2\beta$ is

A $2y^2 + 21y + 52 = 0$

B $2y^2 - 21y + 52 = 0$

C $2y^2 - 21y - 52 = 0$

D $2y^2 + 21y - 52 = 0$

E $2y^2 + 21y - 48 = 0$

15. The complete set of values of x for which
$$|x - 2| < |2x| ,$$
where $x \in \mathbb{R}$, is

A $\{x : x > -2\}$

B $\{x : \frac{2}{3} < x < 2\}$

C $\{x : x < -2\} \cup \{x : \frac{2}{3} < x < 2\}$

D $\{x : x < -2\} \cup \{x : x > \frac{2}{3}\}$

E $\{x : x < -\frac{2}{3}\} \cup \{x : x > 2\}$

16. The general solution of the differential equation

$$\frac{dy}{dx} = \frac{2(y + 1)}{x}$$

is, N being a constant,

A $y = x^2 + N$

B $y = Nx^2 - 1$

C $y = N(x^2 - 1)$

D $y = x^2 + Nx$

E $y = Nx^2 - 2x$

17. Given that $x = \cos^2 t$, $y = \tan t$, then, when $t = \pi/4$,

$\frac{dy}{dx} =$

A 2

B -2

C 4

D -4

E $-\frac{1}{2}$

18.

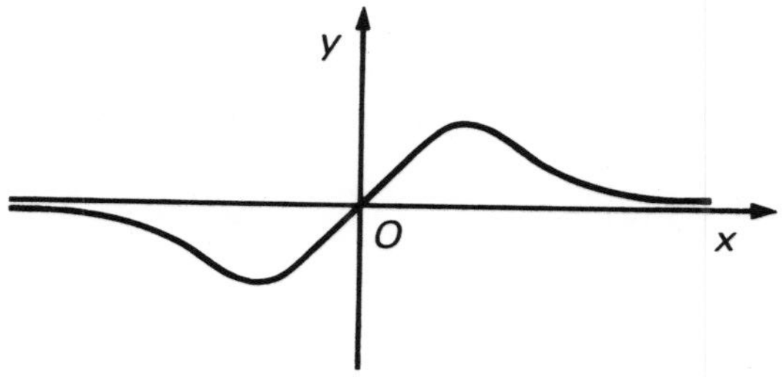

The equation of the curve shown could be

A $y = \tan^{-1}x$

B $y = x\,e^{-x}$

C $y = \frac{x}{1 + x^2}$

D $y = \frac{x^2}{1 + x^4}$

E $y = \frac{\sin x}{x}$

19. The number of solutions, which lie in the range $0 \leqslant x \leqslant 2\pi$, of the equation

$$2\sin^2 x + 7\sin x + 6 = 0,$$

where $x \in \mathbb{R}$, is

A 0

B 1

C 2

D 4

E none of the above

20. $(2\mathbf{i} + 3\mathbf{j} + \mathbf{k}).(\mathbf{i} - 4\mathbf{j} + \mathbf{k}) =$

A $2\mathbf{i} - 12\mathbf{j} + \mathbf{k}$

B 9

C -9

D $9\mathbf{i}$

E $-9\mathbf{i}$

SECTION II

Questions 21–30 **(Ten questions)**

21. $z = x + iy$, where $x, y \in \mathbb{R}$ and $xy \neq 0$.

1 $z\,z^*$ is real

2 $z + z^*$ is real

3 $\dfrac{z^*}{z}$ is real

22. To prove that the curve $y = f(x)$ has a point of inflexion at $x = a$ it is sufficient to show that

1 $f'(a) = 0$

2 $f''(a) = 0$

3 $f'(a - h)$ and $f'(a + h)$, where h is small, are of like sign

23. The points P and Q have position vectors **p** and **q** respectively.

1 The mid-point of PQ has position vector $\frac{1}{2}(\mathbf{p} + \mathbf{q})$

2 The bisector of angle POQ is in the direction of the vector $\dfrac{\mathbf{p}}{|\mathbf{p}|} + \dfrac{\mathbf{q}}{|\mathbf{q}|}$

3 The line PQ is in the direction of the vector $(\mathbf{q} - \mathbf{p})$

24. Which of the following are (is a) geometric series?

1 $1 + 3 + 5 + \ldots + (2r + 1) + \ldots$

2 $1 + 4 + 9 + \ldots + r^2 + \ldots$

3 $\dfrac{1}{4} + \dfrac{1}{16} + \dfrac{1}{64} + \ldots + \dfrac{1}{2^{2r}} + \ldots$

25. $\displaystyle\int_a^b f(x)dx = P, \int_a^b g(x)dx = Q.$

1 $\displaystyle\int_a^b [f(x) - g(x)]dx = P - Q$

2 $\displaystyle\int_a^b ([f(x)]^2 - [g(x)]^2)\,dx = P^2 - Q^2$

3 $\displaystyle\int_a^b \frac{f(x)}{g(x)}\,dx = \frac{P}{Q}$

26.

1 $\dfrac{d^2}{dx^2}(e^{-2x}) = 4e^{-2x}$

2 $\displaystyle\int_0^{\ln 2} e^{2x}dx = \frac{3}{2}$

3 The curve $y = e^{2x}$ has no asymptote(s)

27. Given that

$$x^3 + px^2 + r \equiv (x + \alpha)^2 (x - \beta),$$

where p, r, α, β are non-zero constants, then

1 $2\alpha = \beta$

2 $3\alpha + 2p = 0$

3 $r = -\alpha^2\beta$

28.

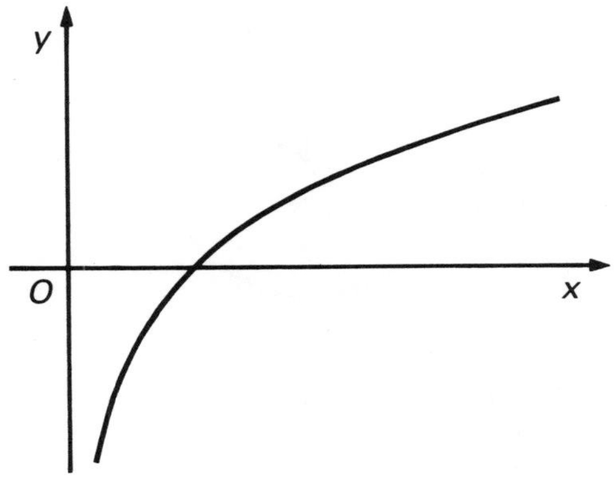

The diagram could be the graph of

1 $y = e^x$

2 $y = \ln x$

3 $x = a^y$, where $a > 0$

29. $y^2 \dfrac{dy}{dx} = -2x$.

1 If $x > 0$ and $y < 0$, then $\dfrac{dy}{dx} < 0$

2 y has a minimum when $x = 0$

3 $y^3 - 3x^2$ is constant

30. Given that x, y and z are the angles of a triangle, which of the following statements is (are) always true?

1 $(x > y) \Rightarrow (\cos x < \cos y)$

2 $(\sin x = \sin y) \Rightarrow (x = y)$

3 $(x < y) \Rightarrow (\sin x < \sin y)$

Test 6

Time allowed: 1 hour

SECTION I

Questions 1–20 **(Twenty questions)**

1. $\sin 5\theta - \sin 9\theta \equiv$

A $-2 \sin 7\theta \cos 2\theta$

B $-2 \sin 2\theta \cos 7\theta$

C $-2 \cos 7\theta \cos 2\theta$

D $2 \sin 2\theta \sin 7\theta$

E $2 \sin 2\theta \cos 7\theta$

2. The modulus of $(1 - i)^6$ is

A 1

B $\sqrt{2}$

C 2

D $2\sqrt{2}$

E 8

3. $\sum_{r=1}^{10} (2r)^2 =$

A 12 100

B 3025

C 2870

D 1540

E 770

4.

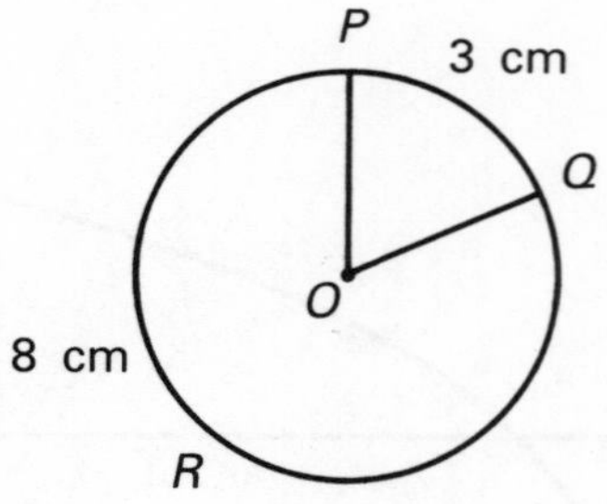

The minor arc PQ is of length 3 cm. The major arc QRP is of length 8 cm.

$\angle POQ =$

A $\frac{3}{8}$ radians

B $\frac{3\pi}{11}$ radians

C $\frac{6\pi}{11}$ radians

D $\frac{33}{2\pi}$ radians

E $\frac{8\pi}{11}$ radians

5. In a convergent geometric progression the first term is 3 and the sum to infinity is 4. The fourth term of the progression is

A $\frac{3}{4}$

B $\frac{3}{64}$

C $\frac{3}{256}$

D $-\frac{3}{64}$

E $-\frac{3}{256}$

6.

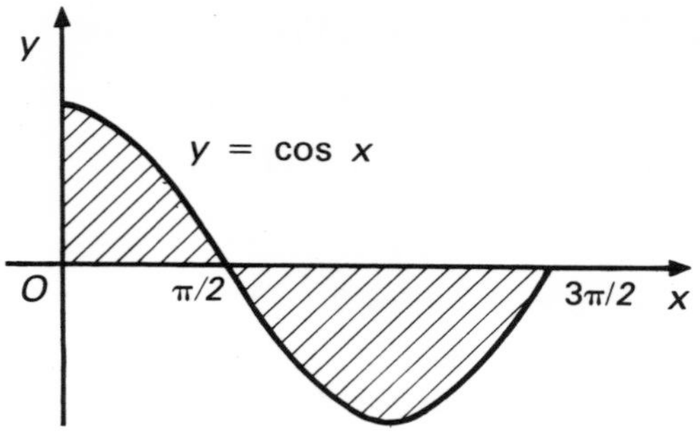

The total area, in square units, of the shaded regions is

A 3

B -1

C 1

D 2

E -2

7. The complete solution set of the inequality

$$2|x| > |x - 1|,$$

where $x \in \mathbb{R}$, is

A $\{x : x < -1\}$

B $\{x : x > \frac{1}{3}\}$

C $\{x : -1 < x < \frac{1}{3}\}$

D $\{x : x < -1\} \cup \{x : x > \frac{1}{3}\}$

E $\{x : x < -\frac{1}{3}\} \cup \{x : x > 1\}$

8. The complex number z has modulus 20 and argument $\tan^{-1}(-4/3)$, where $-\pi/2 < \arg z < \pi/2$.

$z =$

A $12 + 16i$

B $16 + 12i$

C $12 - 16i$

D $16 - 12i$

E $-16 - 12i$

9. An equation of the straight line which passes through the point (1, 0) and through the centre of the circle

$$x^2 + y^2 - 10x + 4y = 0$$

is

A $x - 3y - 1 = 0$

B $x - 2y - 1 = 0$

C $x + 2y - 1 = 0$

D $2x + y + 2 = 0$

E $2x + y - 8 = 0$

10. $\frac{d}{dx}\cos(x^2) =$

A $\sin(x^2)$

B $-\sin(x^2)$

C $\cos 2x$

D $-2x\sin(x^2)$

E $2x\sin(x^2)$

11. $f(x) \equiv (1 - 2x)^{-1} + (1 + x)^{-1}$.

$f(x)$ can be expanded as a series of ascending powers of x if

A $-1 < x < \frac{1}{2}$

B $-1 < x < 1$

C $-\frac{1}{2} \leqslant x \leqslant \frac{1}{2}$

D $-\frac{1}{2} < x < \frac{1}{2}$

E $-2 < x < 2$

12. Given that $f(x) = e^{-x}$, for $x \in \mathbb{R}^+$, then $f^{-1}(x) =$

A e^x

B $-e^x$

C $\ln x$

D $-\ln x$

E $e^{-1/x}$

13. The equation $2x^2 + 5x - 6 = 0$ has roots α and β.

$\alpha^2 + \beta^2 =$

A $\frac{1}{4}$

B $\frac{13}{4}$

C $\frac{25}{4}$

D $\frac{37}{4}$

E $\frac{49}{4}$

14. The radius of a sphere is increasing at a constant rate. When the radius is 20 cm, the rate of increase of the surface area is 30 $cm^2\ s^{-1}$. At this moment the rate of increase of the volume, in $cm^3 s^{-1}$, is

A 300π

B 300

C 200

D 15

E 3

15. Given that

$$f : x \mapsto \frac{e^x}{1 - e^x},\ x \in \mathbb{R}^+,$$

then $f^{-1} : x \mapsto$

A $\ln\left(\frac{x}{x+1}\right)$

B $\ln\left(\frac{x+1}{x}\right)$

C $\frac{x}{x+1}$

D $\frac{1 - e^x}{e^x}$

E $\frac{e^{-x}}{1 - e^{-x}}$

16. The points P, Q and R are collinear.

$$\overrightarrow{OP} = 3\mathbf{i} + \mathbf{j} - \mathbf{k},$$
$$\overrightarrow{OQ} = \mathbf{i} - 2\mathbf{j} + \mathbf{k},$$
$$\overrightarrow{OR} = 2\mathbf{i} + p\mathbf{j} + q\mathbf{k}.$$

A $p = -3, q = 2,$

B $p = -3\frac{1}{2}, q = 2,$

C $p = -\frac{1}{2}, q = 0,$

D $p = 3, q = -2,$

E $p = -\frac{1}{2}, q = 2$

17. Given the following two statements,
(1) $x^2 < 1$,
(2) $x < 1$,
where $x \in \mathbb{R}$, which one of the following statements is always true?

A (1) $\Rightarrow$ (2) but (2) $\not\Rightarrow$ (1)

B (2) $\Rightarrow$ (1) but (1) $\not\Rightarrow$ (2)

C (1) $\Leftrightarrow$ (2)

D (1) $\not\Rightarrow$ (2) and (2) $\not\Rightarrow$ (1)

E None of the above

18. $\int \ln x \, dx =$

A $\frac{1}{x}$ + constant

B $x \ln x$ + constant

C $x \ln x - x$ + constant

D $\frac{1}{x} \ln x$ + constant

E $x \ln x + x$ + constant

19. Given that $a > 0$ and $b^2 < ac$, a sketch of the curve $y = ax^2 + 2bx + c$, could be

A

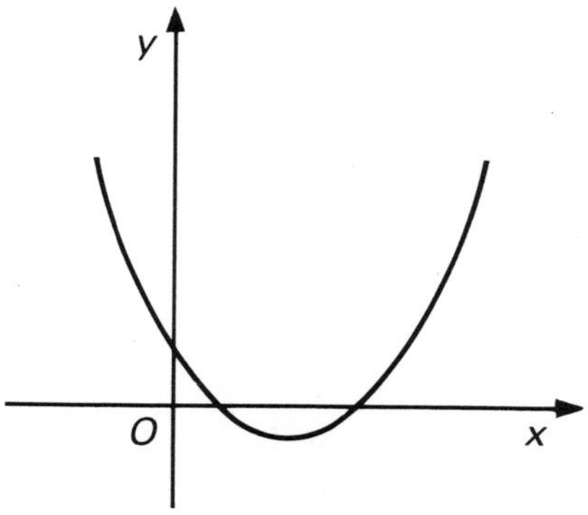

B

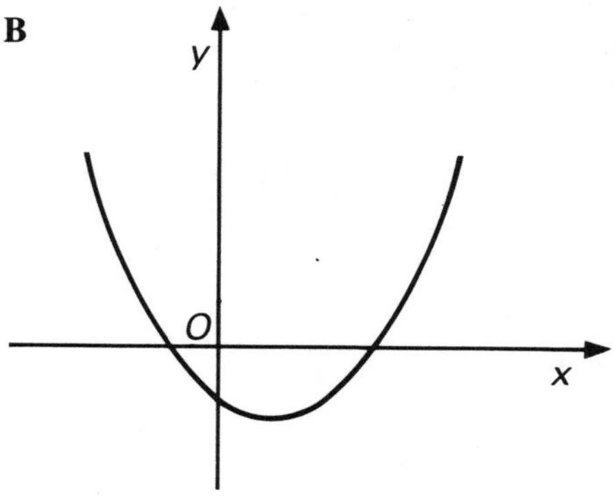

C

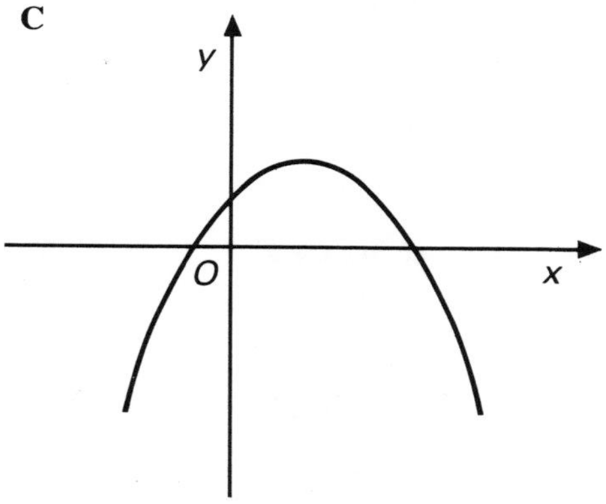

D

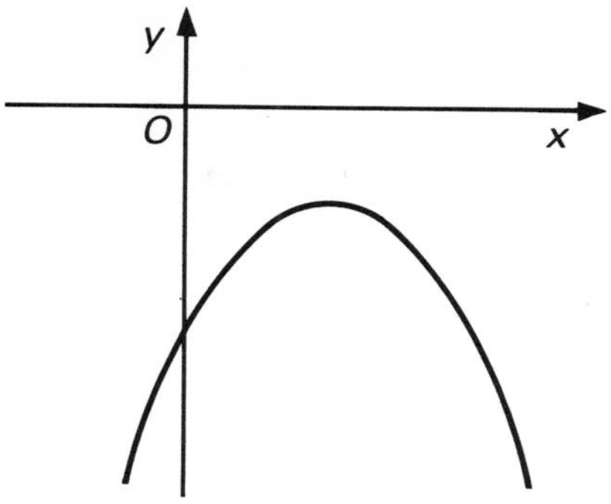

E

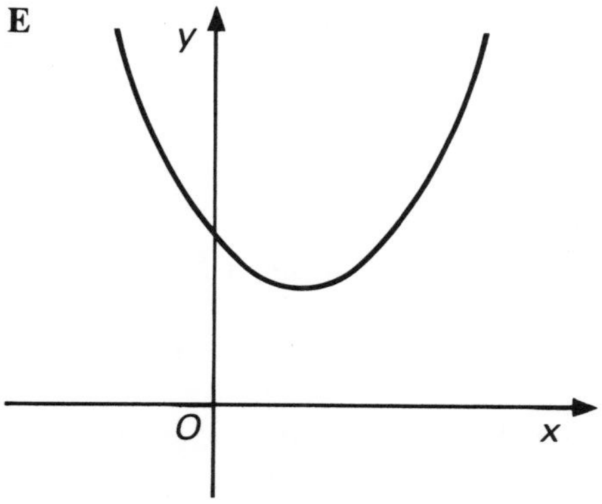

20. The number of different arrangements which can be made using all the letters of the word FOOLS, if the O's are never separated, is

A 120

B 48

C 24

D 20

E 10

SECTION II

Questions 21–30 **(Ten questions)**

21. $z = \dfrac{2 + i}{2 - i}$.

1 $|z| = 1$

2 $\text{Re } z = \dfrac{3}{5}$

3 $\arg z = \dfrac{\pi}{4}$

22. The solutions of the equation

$$2x^3 + 6x^2 - 1 = 0$$

can be found from the intersections of the two graphs

1 $y = 2x^3$ and $y = 6x^2 - 1$

2 $y = 6 - \dfrac{1}{x^2}$ and $y = 2x$

3 $y = x^2(x + 3)$ and $y = \frac{1}{2}$

23. In which of the following differential equations can the variables be separated?

1 $y^2(1 + x)\dfrac{dy}{dx} = (1 - y)x^2$

2 $x\dfrac{dy}{dx} + y = 1 - y^2$

3 $x\dfrac{dy}{dx} = x + y^2$

24. In the geometric series

$$\frac{x-1}{x} + \left(\frac{x-1}{x}\right)^2 + \left(\frac{x-1}{x}\right)^3 + \ldots,$$

where $x > \frac{1}{2}$,

1 each term of the series is less than 1

2 the series converges only when $x < 1$

3 when the series is convergent the sum to infinity is x

25. $f : x \mapsto e^x$ and $x,\ y \in \mathbb{R}^+$.

1 $f(x + y) = f(x) \cdot f(y)$

2 $f^{-1}(xy) = f^{-1}(x) + f^{-1}(y)$

3 $f^{-1}(x^y) = y\, f^{-1}(x)$

26. $f(x) \equiv x^6 + 64$.

1 $(x + 2)$ is a factor of $f(x)$

2 $(x - 2)$ is a factor of $f(x)$

3 $(x^2 + 4)$ is a factor of $f(x)$

27. Given that $y = \dfrac{x}{a + bx}$, where a, b are non-zero constants, then a straight line graph is obtained by plotting

1 $\dfrac{1}{x}$ against $\dfrac{1}{y}$

2 $\dfrac{y}{x}$ against y

3 $\dfrac{x}{y}$ against x

28. A vector equation of the line l is

$$\mathbf{r} = (2\mathbf{i} + 6\mathbf{k}) + t(3\mathbf{i} + 4\mathbf{k}),$$

where t is a parameter.

1 l passes through the origin O

2 l is perpendicular to Oy

3 The vector $(3\mathbf{i} + 4\mathbf{k})$ is parallel to l

29. $S = \sum_{r=10}^{19} r^2$.

1 $\sum_{r=10}^{19} 2r^2 = 2S$

2 $\sum_{r=10}^{19} (r^2 + 1) = S + 9$

3 $\sum_{r=10}^{19} r^4 = S^2$

30. $f : x \mapsto \frac{1}{2}(e^x + e^{-x}),\ x \in \mathbb{R}$.
$g : x \mapsto \frac{1}{2}(e^x - e^{-x}),\ x \in \mathbb{R}$.

1 $f(2x) = [f(x)]^2 - [g(x)]^2$

2 $g(2x) = 2\, f(x) \cdot g(x)$

3 $-1 < \dfrac{g(x)}{f(x)} < 1$

Test 7

Time allowed: 1 hour

SECTION I

Questions 1–20 **(Twenty questions)**

1. An equation of a circle, with radius r and centre (a, b), is

A $x^2 + y^2 = r^2 - a^2 - b^2$

B $x^2 + y^2 + ax + by = r^2 - a^2 - b^2$

C $x^2 + y^2 - ax - by = r^2 - a^2 - b^2$

D $x^2 + y^2 - 2ax - 2by = r^2 - a^2 - b^2$

E $x^2 + y^2 + 2ax + 2by = r^2 - a^2 - b^2$

2. The complete solution set of the inequality

$$|x - 1| > |x| ,$$

where $x \in \mathbb{R}$, is

A $\{x : x > \frac{1}{2}\}$

B $\{x : x < 1\}$

C $\{x : x < \frac{1}{2}\}$

D $\{x : x < 0\}$

E none of the above

3. $\dfrac{1 - 2\cos^2\theta}{1 - 2\sin^2\theta} \equiv$

A -1

B $\dfrac{\cos\theta - \sin\theta}{\cos\theta + \sin\theta}$

C $\dfrac{\cos\theta + \sin\theta}{\cos\theta - \sin\theta}$

D $\dfrac{\sin\theta - \cos\theta}{\sin\theta + \cos\theta}$

E $\dfrac{\tan^2\theta - 1}{\tan^2\theta + 1}$

4. Given that $\tan\alpha = 3/4$ and $\tan\beta = 4/3$, where α and β are both acute, then $\sin(\alpha + \beta) =$

A $\dfrac{7}{5}$

B $\dfrac{24}{25}$

C $\dfrac{7}{25}$

D 0

E 1

5. $\displaystyle\int \frac{1}{\sqrt{(\frac{1}{9} - x^2)}}\,dx =$

A $\sin^{-1}\left(\dfrac{x}{3}\right)$ + constant

B $\sin^{-1}(3x)$ + constant

C $\sin^{-1}\left(\dfrac{3}{x}\right)$ + constant

D $\frac{3}{2}\ln(\frac{1}{9} - x^2)$ + constant

E $\frac{3}{2}\ln\left(\dfrac{1 + 3x}{1 - 3x}\right)$ + constant

6. $\dfrac{d}{dx}(\ln\tan x) =$

A $\ln(\sec^2 x)$

B $\cot x$

C $\dfrac{2}{\sin 2x}$

D $\dfrac{1}{\sin 2x}$

E $\sec x$

7. Given that the roots of the quadratic equation

$$ax^2 + bx + c = 0,$$

where $abc \neq 0$, are α and β, then the roots of the equation

$$16cx^2 + 4bx + a = 0$$

are

A $\frac{1}{4\alpha}$ and $\frac{1}{4\beta}$

B $-\frac{1}{4\alpha}$ and $-\frac{1}{4\beta}$

C $\frac{\alpha}{4}$ and $\frac{\beta}{4}$

D $\frac{4}{\alpha}$ and $\frac{4}{\beta}$

E 4α and 4β

8. $\frac{5 - i}{4 - 3i} =$

A $\frac{1}{5}(23 + 11i)$

B $\frac{1}{7}(23 + 11i)$

C $\frac{1}{7}(23 - 11i)$

D $\frac{1}{25}(23 - 11i)$

E $\frac{1}{25}(23 + 11i)$

9. Given that

$$(\lg x)^2 - 4(\lg x) + 3 = 0,$$

where $x \in \mathbb{R}^+$, then
$x =$

A 1 or 3

B 10 or 1000

C 1 or 1000

D $\frac{1}{10}$ or $\frac{1}{1000}$

E 10 or $\frac{1}{1000}$

10.

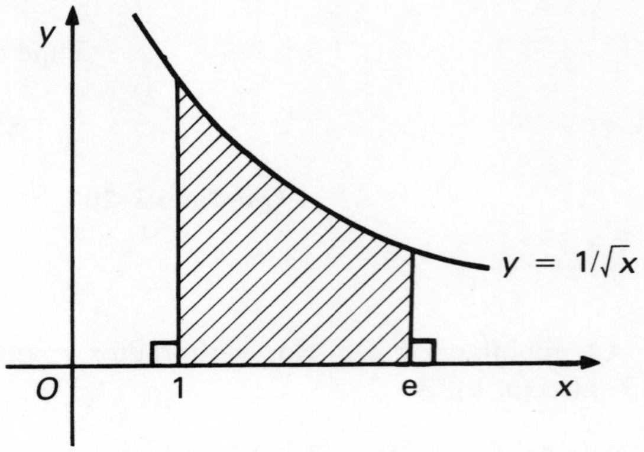

The volume, in cubic units, generated when the shaded region is rotated completely about Ox is

A π

B $\pi(1 - e^{-2})$

C $2(e^{1/2} - 1)$

D πe

E $\pi(e - 1)$

11. The general solution of the differential equation

$$\frac{dy}{dx} + y = 1$$

is, P being an arbitrary constant,

A $2x + (1 - y)^2 = P$

B $2x - (1 - y)^2 = P$

C $y = 1 + Pe^x$

D $y = 1 + Pe^{-x}$

E $y = Pe^{-x} - 1$

12. The number of different permutations of the letters of the word ROTTEN is

A 6!

B (6!)/2

C (5!) × 2

D 5!

E (5!)/2

13. The sum to infinity of a geometric progression of positive terms is 3. When the second term of the progression is subtracted from the first term the result is 4/3. The common ratio of the progression is

A $\frac{1}{4}$

B $\frac{1}{3}$

C $\frac{4}{9}$

D $\frac{1}{2}$

E $\frac{1}{3}$ or $\frac{5}{3}$

14. Given that $\mathbf{a} = (3\mathbf{i} + 4\mathbf{j})$, $\mathbf{b} = (2\mathbf{i} - \mathbf{j})$, $\mathbf{x} = (\mathbf{i} + 5\mathbf{j})$ and $\mathbf{x} = s\mathbf{a} + t\mathbf{b}$,
then the scalars s and t are given by

A $s = -1, \quad t = -1$

B $s = -1, \quad t = 1$

C $s = 1, \quad t = -1$

D $s = 1, \quad t = 1$

E $s = \sqrt{5}, \quad t = 5$

15. All solutions of the simultaneous equations
$2 \cos \theta - \sqrt{3} = 0, \qquad 2 \sin \theta + 1 = 0$
are obtained by taking all integer values of n in

A $n\pi - (-1)^n \frac{\pi}{6}$

B $2n\pi \pm \frac{\pi}{6}$

C $2n\pi + (-1)^n \frac{\pi}{6}$

D $2n\pi - \frac{\pi}{3}$

E $2n\pi - \frac{\pi}{6}$

16. Given that

$$\frac{3^x}{9^y} = 27 \text{ and } 5^x = \frac{1}{5^{y+1}},$$

where $x, y \in \mathbb{R}$, then y

A $= -4$

B $= 4$

C $= 3$

D $= -4/3$

E cannot be found

17. The number of asymptotes of the curve $y = \tan x$, where $x \in \mathbb{R}$, is

A 0

B 2

C 4

D 6

E more than 6

18. $\frac{x-1}{x(x+1)} < 0$ for all finite values of x in the interval

A $x > 1$

B $x < 1$

C $x < -1$

D $x > -1$

E $x > 0$

19. The graph of $y = x - \frac{1}{x}$ could be

A

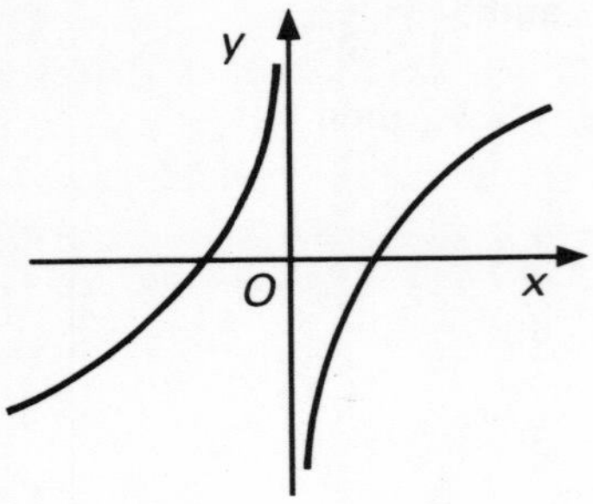

B

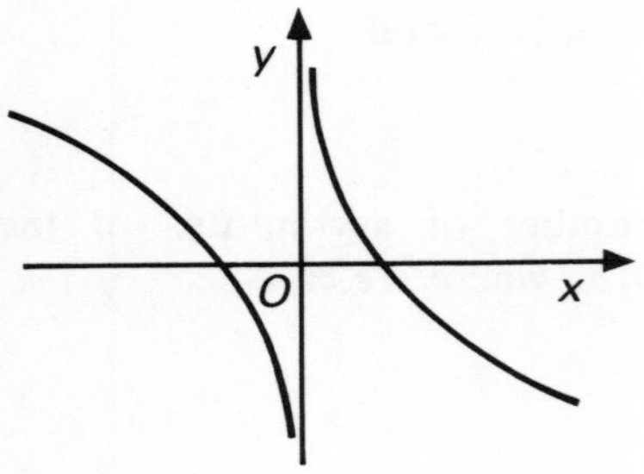

C

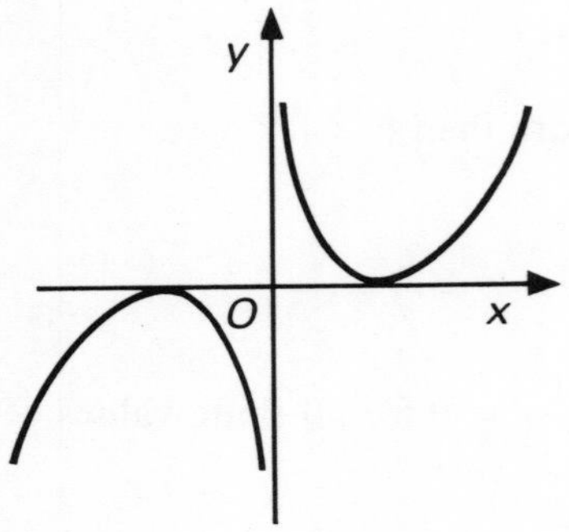

D

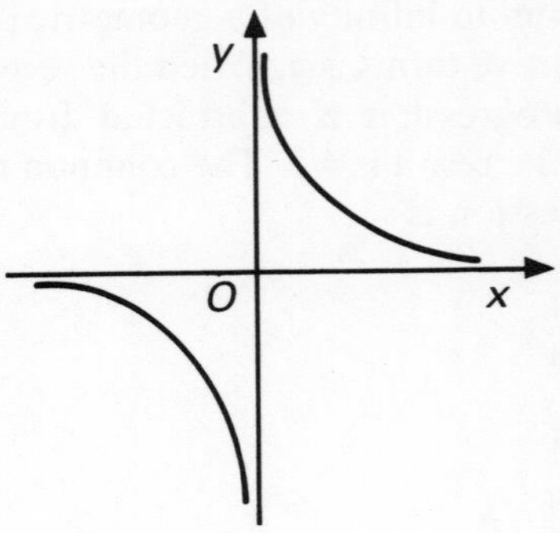

E

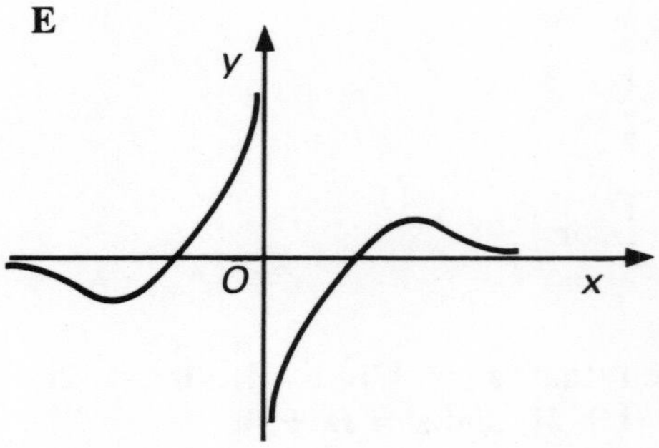

20. Which one of the following expressions is not identically equal to any one of the others?

A $\frac{2 \tan \theta}{1 + \tan^2\theta}$

B $\frac{2 \sin \theta \cos \theta}{\cos^2\theta - \sin^2\theta}$

C $\tan 2\theta$

D $\frac{2 \cot \theta}{\cot^2\theta - 1}$

E $\frac{2 \sin \theta \cos \theta}{2 \cos^2\theta - 1}$

SECTION II

Questions 21–30 **(Ten questions)**

21. The graph of $y = x + \frac{1}{x}$

1 does not intersect either coordinate axis

2 has point symmetry about the origin

3 has two asymptotes

22. $f(x) \equiv x^3 - x^2 - x + 1$.

1 If $x > 0$, then $f(x) > 0$

2 $(x - 1)$ is a factor of $f(x)$

3 $f(x) = 0$ for just two distinct real values of x

23.

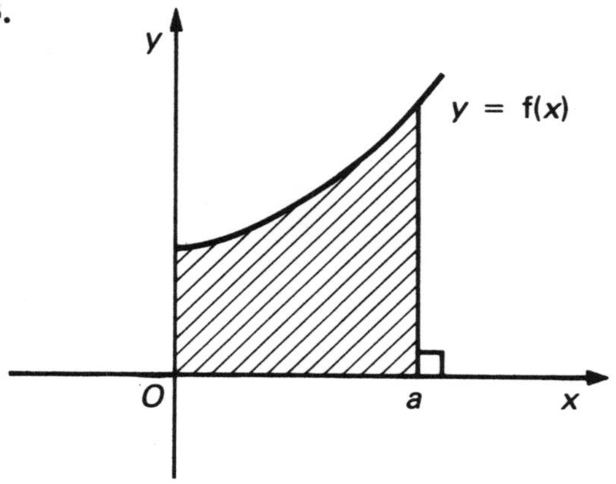

The shaded region bounded by the curve $y = f(x)$, the coordinate axes and the line $x = a$

1 has area $\int_0^a f(x)dx$ square units

2 generates volume $\pi\int_0^a [f(x)]^2\,dx$ cubic units when rotated completely about Ox

3 generates volume $\pi\int_{f(0)}^{f(a)} x^2dy$ cubic units when rotated completely about Oy

24. Given that $y = 3^{x+1}$, a straight line graph through the origin is obtained by plotting

1 $x + 1$ against $\ln y$

2 x against $\ln y$

3 $\ln x$ against $\ln y$

25. Which of the following equations could be solved graphically by finding the intersection(s) of the curve $y = \ln x$ and a suitably chosen straight line?

1 $\ln x = \dfrac{1}{x}$

2 $\ln x = 3$

3 $3x = e^x$

26. A plane passes through the point with position vector **a** and is parallel to each of the non-parallel vectors **b** and **c**. The normal to the plane is in the direction of the unit vector $\hat{\mathbf{n}}$.

1 The distance of the plane from the origin is $\mathbf{a}\,.\,\hat{\mathbf{n}}$

2 The equation of the plane can be written in the form,
$$\mathbf{r} = \mathbf{a} + s\mathbf{b} + t\mathbf{c},$$
where s and t are parameters

3 $\hat{\mathbf{n}}\,.\,(\mathbf{b} - \mathbf{c}) = 0$

27. $x = e^t + e^{-t}$, $y = e^t - e^{-t}$, where $t \in \mathbb{R}$.

1 $x^2 - y^2 = 4$

2 $\dfrac{dy}{dx} = \dfrac{x}{y}$

3 $xy > 0$ for all t

28. $f : x \mapsto \sin^{-1}x$, where $-1 \leqslant x \leqslant 1$.

1 $f^{-1} : x \mapsto \operatorname{cosec} x$

2 $[f(x) = \tfrac{1}{2}] \Rightarrow [x = \pi/6]$

3 The gradient of the graph of f at the origin is 1

29. The first, third and last terms of an arithmetic progression are 2, 8 and 56 respectively. For this progression

1 the tenth term is 29

2 the number of terms is 18

3 the sum of the terms of the progression is 522

30. $(1 + ax)^k$ can be expanded as an infinite series in ascending powers of x when

1 $k \in \mathbb{Z}^+$

2 $|a| < 1$, $k < 0$

3 $|x| < \dfrac{1}{|a|}$, $k < 0$

Test 8

Time allowed: 1 hour

SECTION I

Questions 1–20 **(Twenty questions)**

1. Given that $x \in \mathbb{R}$ and $2e^{2x} - 3e^x + 1 = 0$, then

A $x = 1$ or $\frac{1}{2}$

B $x = 0$ or $\ln 2$

C $x = 1$ or $-\ln 2$

D $x = 0$ or $-\ln 2$

E x cannot be found

2. The gradients of the tangents from the origin to the circle

$$x^2 + y^2 + 10y + 16 = 0,$$

are

A $\pm\dfrac{3}{4}$

B $\pm\dfrac{4}{3}$

C $\pm\dfrac{3}{5}$

D $\pm\dfrac{5}{3}$

E $\pm\dfrac{5}{4}$

3. Given that $x \in \mathbb{R}$, which one of the following is *not* an even function of x?

A $f: x \mapsto |3x|$

B $f: x \mapsto \sin^2 x$

C $f: x \mapsto \cos x$

D $f: x \mapsto x^2 - 1$

E $f: x \mapsto (x - 1)^2$

4. $\displaystyle\int \frac{x^2}{(x^3 + 1)^{1/2}}\,dx =$

A $\frac{1}{3}\ln(x^3 + 1)^{1/2}$ + constant

B $\frac{2}{3}\ln(x^3 + 1)^{1/2}$ + constant

C $\frac{2}{3}(x^3 + 1)^{1/2}$ + constant

D $\frac{1}{6}(x^3 + 1)^{1/2}$ + constant

E $\frac{1}{3}(x^3 + 1)^{1/2}$ + constant

5. The complete set of values of x for which

$$(x + 3)(x^2 - 9) > 0,$$

where $x \in \mathbb{R}$, is

A $\{x : x > 3\}$

B $\{x : x > -3\}$

C $\{x : -3 < x < 3\}$

D $\{x : x < -3\} \cup \{x : x > 3\}$

E $\{x : x < -3\}$

6. The general solution of the differential equation

$$\frac{dy}{dx} + \frac{x + 2}{y + 2} = 0$$

is, P being an arbitrary constant,

A $x^2 - y^2 + 4x - 4y = P$

B $x^2 - y^2 + 2x - 2y = P$

C $y + 2 = \dfrac{P}{x + 2}$

D $x^2 + y^2 + 2x + 2y = P$

E $x^2 + y^2 + 4x + 4y = P$

7. $\lim_{x \to \infty} \dfrac{(4x + 3)(2x + 5)}{(x + 3)(x + 5)}$

A $= 15$

B $= 8$

C $= 1$

D $= 0$

E does not exist

8. Given that $x = t^2$, $y = t$, then

$\dfrac{d^2y}{dx^2} =$

A 0

B $-\dfrac{1}{2t^2}$

C $\dfrac{1}{4t^2}$

D $-\dfrac{1}{4t^3}$

E $-\dfrac{1}{t}$

9. All solutions of the equation

$$\tan x = -\sqrt{3}$$

are obtained by taking all integer values of n in

A $n\pi - \pi/3$

B $2n\pi \pm \pi/3$

C $n\pi + (-1)^{n+1}\pi/3$

D $n\pi - \pi/6$

E $n\pi + \pi/6$

10. The number of 4 letter code words which can be made using the letters P, Q, R, S, if repetitions are allowed, is

A 16

B 24

C 64

D 128

E 256

11. Given that $\overrightarrow{OP} = \mathbf{p}$, $\overrightarrow{OQ} = \mathbf{q}$ and the points O, P, Q are not collinear, which one of the following points, whose position vectors are given, is not collinear with P and Q?

A $\frac{1}{2}\mathbf{p} + \frac{1}{2}\mathbf{q}$

B $3\mathbf{p} - 2\mathbf{q}$

C $\mathbf{p} - \mathbf{q}$

D $\frac{1}{3}\mathbf{p} + \frac{2}{3}\mathbf{q}$

E $2\mathbf{p} - \mathbf{q}$

12. The gradient of the normal to the curve $y = e^{-\cos x}$ at the point where $x = \pi/3$ is

A $\dfrac{\sqrt{3}}{2e^{1/2}}$

B $-\dfrac{2e^{1/2}}{\sqrt{3}}$

C $\dfrac{1}{2e^{(\sqrt{3})/2}}$

D $\dfrac{2e^{1/2}}{\sqrt{3}}$

E $-e^{-1/2}$

13.

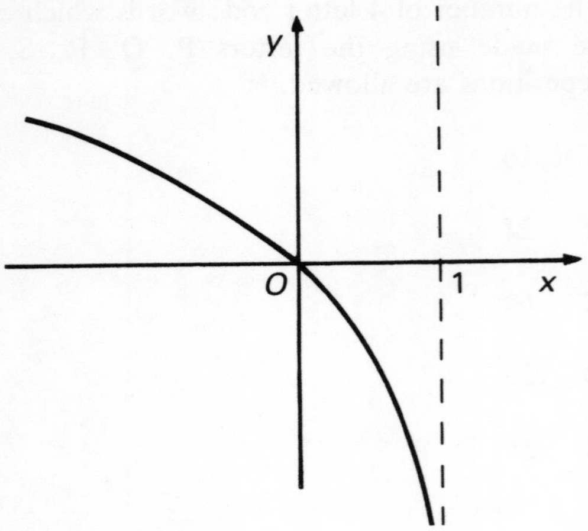

The graph could be a sketch of the curve

A $y = \dfrac{1}{x - 1}$

B $y = \dfrac{1}{1 - x}$

C $y = \ln(1 - x)$

D $y = \ln(x - 1)$

E $y = \ln(1 - x^2)$

14. Given that

$$f(x) \equiv ax^3 + bx^2 + cx + d,$$

where $a, b, c, d \in \mathbb{Z}$ and are constants, and $f(-3/2) = 0$, which one of the following must be a factor of $f(x)$?

A $x - \frac{3}{2}$

B $2 - 3x$

C $3 - 2x$

D $2x + 3$

E $3x + 2$

15. An equation of the tangent to the circle

$$x^2 + y^2 - 2x + 3y = 0$$

at the origin is

A $2x - 3y = 0$

B $3x + 2y = 0$

C $2x + 3y = 0$

D $3x - 2y = 0$

E none of the above

16. Given that $0 < \theta < \pi/2$, then the argument of $\dfrac{\cos\theta - i\sin\theta}{\cos\theta + i\sin\theta}$ is

A $-\theta$

B θ

C $\pi - 2\theta$

D 2θ

E -2θ

17. The roots of the equation

$$2x^2 + 6x + 7 = 0$$

are α and β. Then $|\alpha - \beta| =$

A $\sqrt{5}$

B $2\sqrt{5}$

C $4\sqrt{5}$

D $\sqrt{(5/2)}$

E $1/(2\sqrt{5})$

18. The sum of all the positive even numbers less than 100 is

A 5000

B 4900

C 2550

D 2500

E 2450

19. The number of solutions, which lie in the range $0 \leqslant \theta \leqslant 4\pi$, of the equation

$$\cos^2\theta - 3\cos\theta + 2 = 0$$

is

A 2

B 3

C 4

D 5

E more than 5

20. Given the following two statements,
(1) $(x - 2)(3 - x) < 0$,
(2) $x > 3$,
where $x \in \mathbb{R}$, which one of the following statements is always true?

A (1) $\Rightarrow$ (2) but (2) $\not\Rightarrow$ (1)

B (2) $\Rightarrow$ (1) but (1) $\not\Rightarrow$ (2)

C (1) $\Leftrightarrow$ (2)

D (1) $\not\Rightarrow$ (2) and (2) $\not\Rightarrow$ (1)

E None of the above

SECTION II

Questions 21–30 **(Ten questions)**

21. $(x + iy)^2 = 3 + 4i$, where $x, y \in \mathbb{R}$.

1 $x^2 + y^2 = 3$

2 $xy = 2$

3 $(x - iy)^2 = 3 - 4i$

22. The curve $x^2 + y^2 + 2x + 4y + 4 = 0$

1 is a circle

2 touches the y-axis

3 does not pass through any point (x,y) for which $x \geqslant 0$, $y \geqslant 0$

23. Given that p, q, x and y are non-zero real numbers and

$$\frac{p}{q} > \frac{x}{y},$$

which of the following inequalities must necessarily be true?

1 $\dfrac{p}{x} > \dfrac{q}{y}$

2 $\dfrac{q}{p} < \dfrac{y}{x}$

3 $\dfrac{py - qx}{qy} > 0$

24. The loci whose equations are

$$(x - 2y - 2) + \lambda(y + 2) = 0,$$

where λ is a variable parameter,

1 are all straight lines

2 all pass through the point $(2, -2)$

3 include the line $x = 2$

25. $\overrightarrow{OP} = (-2\mathbf{i} + 3\mathbf{j} + \mathbf{k})$,
$\overrightarrow{OQ} = (3\mathbf{i} - 2\mathbf{j} + \mathbf{k})$.

1 $\overrightarrow{PQ} = -5\mathbf{i} + 5\mathbf{j}$

2 $\overrightarrow{OP} \cdot \overrightarrow{OQ} = -11$

3 $\cos\angle POQ = -\dfrac{11}{14}$

26. Given that $xy = ax^2 + b$, where a, b are non-zero constants, then a straight line graph is obtained by plotting

1 xy against x^2

2 y/x against $1/x^2$

3 $\log(xy)$ against $\log(x^2)$

27. f and g map $\mathbb{R}$ into $\mathbb{R}$.
$f(x) = \cos x$,
$g(x) = x^3$.

1 gf is an odd function

2 fg is a periodic function

3 The range of gf is $[-1, 1]$

28. The equation $e^x = \sin x$, where $x \in \mathbb{R}$,

1 has no positive roots

2 has an infinite number of negative roots

3 has two roots in the interval $(-\pi, 0)$

29. $x = 1 + \cos^2\theta - \cos^4\theta$,
$y = 1 + \sin^2\theta - \sin^4\theta$.

1 $x - y = 0$

2 $x + y = 2\cos^2\theta \sin^2\theta$

3 $x = 1 + \frac{1}{4}\sin^2 2\theta$

30. The graph of $y = x \sin x$

1 is symmetrical about the y-axis

2 touches the x-axis at the origin

3 touches the line $y = x$ at the point $(\pi/2, \pi/2)$

Test 9 (Further Mathematics)

Time allowed: 1 hour

The numerical value of g should be understood to be available for questions in any section if required. Take g as 10 ms^{-2} unless otherwise given.

SECTION I

Questions 1–10 **(Ten questions)**

1.

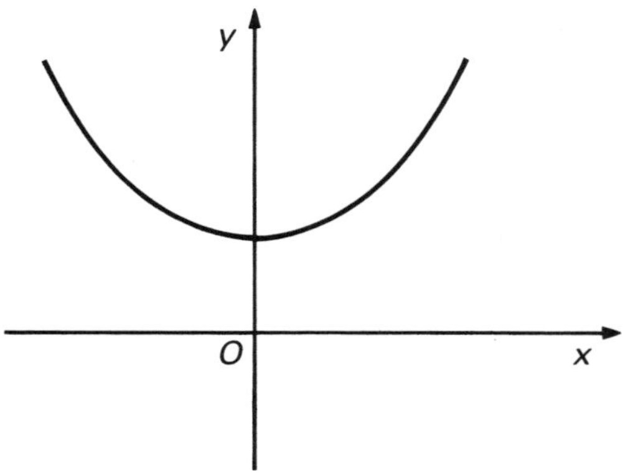

The given diagram could be the graph of

A $y = \sinh x$

B $y = \cosh x$

C $y = \tanh x$

D $y = \text{sech}\, x$

E $y = \text{cosech}\, x$

2. The general solution of the differential equation

$$4\frac{d^2y}{dx^2} + 4\frac{dy}{dx} + y = 0$$

is, P and Q being arbitrary constants,

A $y = P\,e^{-2x} + Q\,e^{2x}$

B $y = P\,e^{-x/2} + Q\,e^{x/2}$

C $y = (P + xQ)e^{x/2}$

D $y = (P + xQ)e^{-2x}$

E $y = (P + xQ)e^{-x/2}$

3. Of the functions $\sinh x$, $\cosh x$, $\tanh x$, $\text{sech}\, x$, $\text{cosech}\, x$, $\coth x$,

A 2 are even functions and 4 are odd functions

B 3 are even functions and 3 are odd functions

C 4 are even functions and 2 are odd functions

D 2 are odd functions, 2 are even functions and 2 are neither

E none of the above statements is true

4.

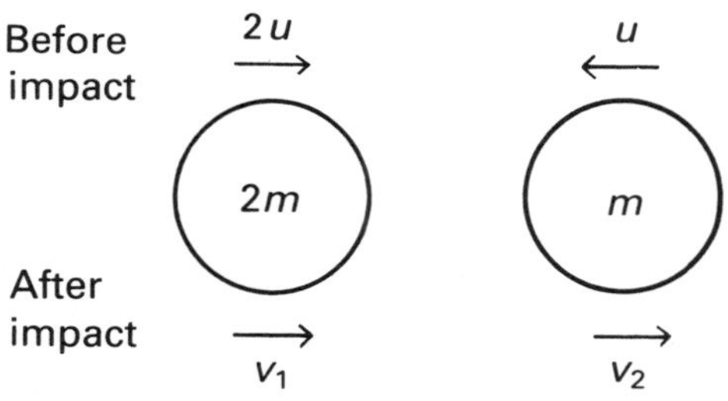

The spheres collide directly as shown and the coefficient of restitution is $\frac{1}{3}$.

$v_1 =$

A $8u/9$

B $5u/3$

C $4u/3$

D $2u/3$

E 0

5. The graph of $y = \ln(1 + x^2)$ could be

A

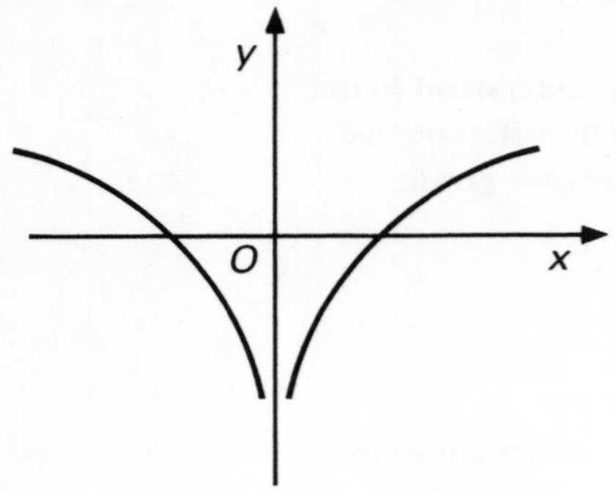

B

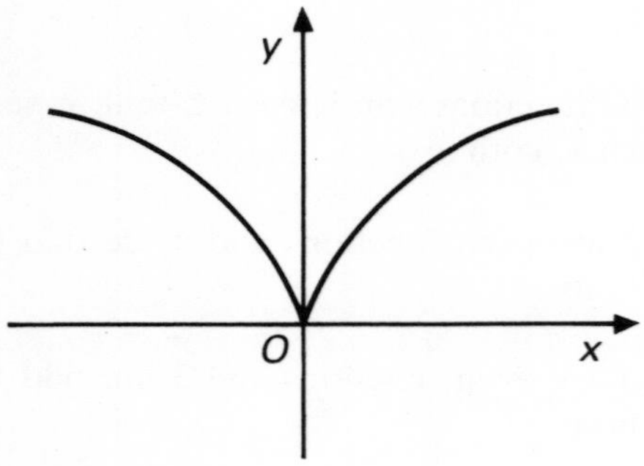

C

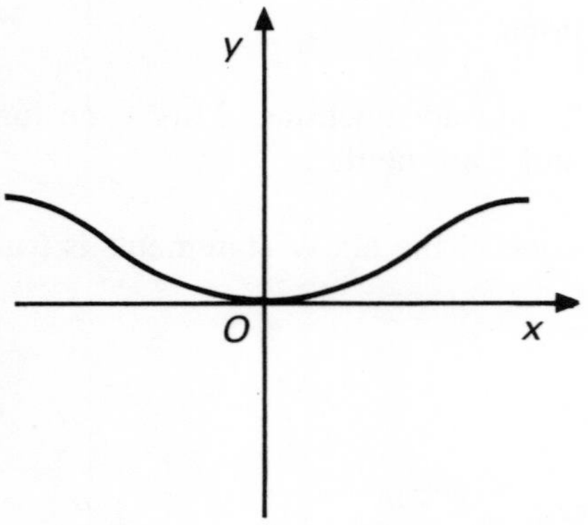

D

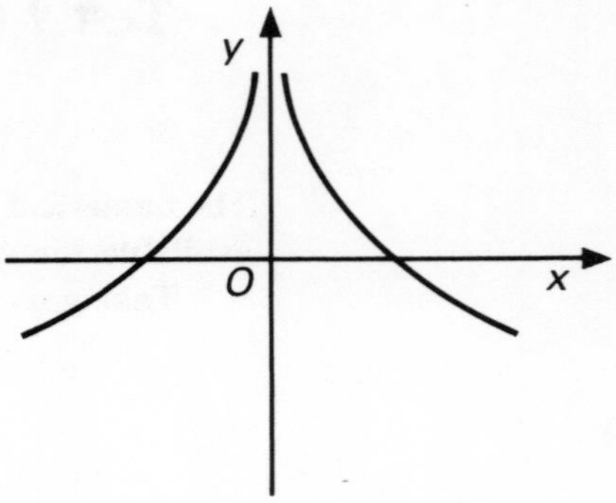

E

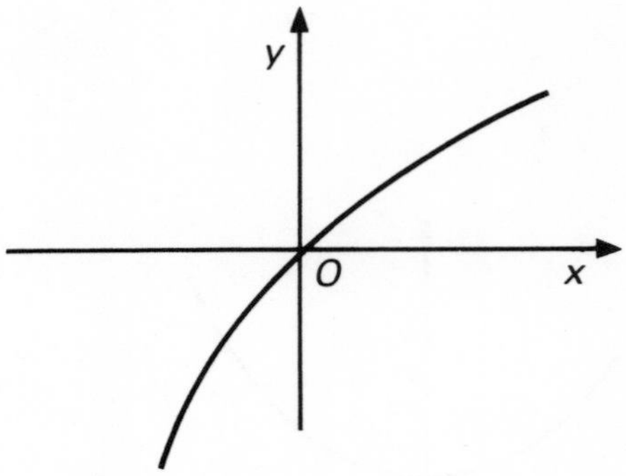

6. In the Argand diagram the locus of points satisfying the equation

$$\left|\frac{z - \mathrm{i}}{z + 2}\right| = 1$$

is

A a straight line

B a circle

C a parabola

D an ellipse

E a hyperbola

7. An integrating factor of the differential equation

$$\frac{\mathrm{d}y}{\mathrm{d}x} - y \cot x = \sin x$$

is

A $\sin x$

B $\operatorname{cosec} x$

C $\mathrm{e}^{-\cot x}$

D $\cos x$

E $\sec x$

8. A uniform rod PQ, of mass m and length $2a$, is rotating in a plane with angular speed ω about the end P. Its moment of momentum about P is of magnitude

A $ma^2\omega/3$

B $ma^2\omega/2$

C $4ma^2\omega/3$

D $ma^2\omega^2/6$

E $2ma^2\omega^2/3$

9. Four coins are to be tossed simultaneously. The probability that there will be an odd number of tails is

A $\frac{2}{5}$

B $\frac{1}{8}$

C $\frac{1}{4}$

D $\frac{1}{2}$

E $\frac{5}{8}$

10. A particle moves along Ox with velocity v, where $v = kx^3$ and k is a constant. At time $t = 0$, $x = a$, where $a > 0$. Then $kt =$

A $(x^2 - a^2)/(a^2x^2)$

B $(x^4 - a^4)/(3a^4x^4)$

C $(a^4 - x^4)/(3a^4x^4)$

D $(a^2 - x^2)/(2a^2x^2)$

E $(x^2 - a^2)/(2a^2x^2)$

SECTION II

Questions 11–15 **(Five questions)**

11. z_1 and z_2 are complex numbers.

1 $|z_1 - z_2| \geqslant |z_1| - |z_2|$

2 $|z_1 + z_2| \leqslant |z_1| + |z_2|$

3 $(z_1z_2)^* = z_1^* \, z_2^*$

12. $u_r = \dfrac{1}{r^2(r^2 + 1)}$.

1 $u_r = \dfrac{1}{r^2} - \dfrac{1}{r^2 + 1}$

2 The series $\sum_{r=1}^{\infty} u_r$ converges

3 $\sum_{r=1}^{10} u_r = \dfrac{100}{101}$

13. $\dfrac{d\mathbf{v}}{dt} + 2\mathbf{v} = \mathbf{0}$, and $\mathbf{v} = (\mathbf{j} + \mathbf{k})$ when $t = 0$.

1 $\mathbf{v} \cdot \mathbf{i} = 0$

2 $\mathbf{v} \cdot \mathbf{j} = e^{2t}$

3 $\mathbf{v} \times \mathbf{k} = \mathbf{i}\, e^{2t}$

14. The probability density function $p(x)$ of a random variable X is such that $p(x) = 0$ for $x \leqslant 0$ and for $x \geqslant a$.

1 The mean of the distribution is $a/2$

2 $\int_0^a p(x)dx = 1$

3 The variance of the distribution is

$$\int_0^a x^2\, p(x)dx - \left[\int_0^a xp(x)dx\right]^2$$

15.

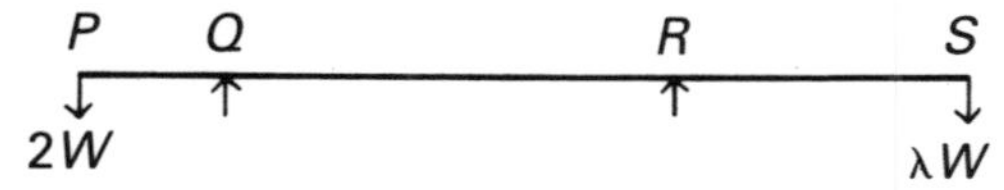

The uniform beam $PQRS$, where $PQ = a$, $QR = 3a$ and $RS = 2a$, rests horizontally in equilibrium on supports at Q and R. The weight of the beam is W and loads of weight $2W$ and λW are hung from P and S respectively.

1 The force exerted on the support at Q is of magnitude $5\lambda W/3$

2 The force exerted on the support at R is of magnitude $(9 - 2\lambda)W/3$

3 $\lambda \leqslant 4\frac{1}{2}$

SECTION III

Questions 16–20 **(Five questions)**

16. For the differential equation

$$\frac{d^2y}{dx^2} + ny = 12x,$$

where n is a constant,

1 the complementary function is of the form $P\,e^{2x} + Q\,e^{-2x}$

2 the particular integral is $3x$

17. Forces $\mathbf{F}_1$, $\mathbf{F}_2$, $\mathbf{F}_3$ act at the points with position vectors $\mathbf{r}_1$, $\mathbf{r}_2$, $\mathbf{r}_3$ respectively, where $\mathbf{F}_1$, $\mathbf{F}_2$, $\mathbf{F}_3$, $\mathbf{r}_1$, $\mathbf{r}_2$, $\mathbf{r}_3$ are non-zero.

1 The forces are in equilibrium

2 $\mathbf{r}_1 \times \mathbf{F}_1 + \mathbf{r}_2 \times \mathbf{F}_2 + \mathbf{r}_3 \times \mathbf{F}_3 = \mathbf{0}$

18. 1 X and Y are independent events

2 $P(Y) = P(X|Y)$

19. $\mathbf{P}$, $\mathbf{Q}$ and $\mathbf{R}$ are non-singular 3×3 matrices.

1 $\mathbf{S} = \mathbf{PQR}$

2 $\mathbf{S}^{-1} = \mathbf{R}^{-1}\mathbf{Q}^{-1}\mathbf{P}^{-1}$

20. A particle P falls freely in a resisting medium, where v is the speed and k is a constant.

1 The terminal speed of P is $\sqrt{(g/k)}$

2 The resistance of the medium to the motion of P is of magnitude kv^2 per unit mass

SECTION IV

Questions 21–25 **(Five questions)**

21. Evaluate $\int_0^8 f(x)\,dx$.

1 $f(x)$ is periodic with period 4

2 $f(x)$ is an even function

3 $f(x) = x$ for $0 \leqslant x < 2$

4 $f(x) = 4 - x$ for $2 \leqslant x < 4$

22. Find the least distance between P and Q.

1 The velocity of P relative to R is given

2 The velocity of Q relative to R is given

3 The velocity of R is given

4 At time $t = 0$, the vector $\overrightarrow{PQ}$ is given

23. $\dfrac{dv}{dt} = a + bt + c\cos(2\pi t)$.

Find the value of v when $t = 2$.

1 v is given when $t = 0$

2 v is given when $t = -\frac{1}{4}$

3 v is given when $t = -\frac{1}{2}$

4 v is given when $t = -1$

24. Determine the number of real roots of the equation $f(x) = 0$, where

$$f(x) \equiv x^3 + ax^2 + bx + c,$$

$$a, b, c \in \mathbb{Z}, \quad p, q \in \mathbb{R} \quad \text{and} \quad p \neq q.$$

1 $f'(p) = 0$

2 $f'(q) = 0$

3 $f(p) > 0$

4 $f(q) < 0$

25. Find the kinetic energy of a uniform, solid, circular cylinder which is rotating about a generator with constant angular speed.

1 The angular speed of the cylinder is given

2 The mass of the cylinder is given

3 The radius of the cylinder is given

4 The length of the cylinder is given

SECTION V

Questions 26–30 **(Five questions)**

26. Prove that the equation

$$z^3 + az + b = 0,$$

where $a, b \in \mathbb{R}$, has only one real root.

1 $a > 0$

2 $b > 0$

27. Show that events X and Y are independent.

1 $\mathrm{P}(Y|X) = \mathrm{P}(Y)$

2 $\mathrm{P}(X \cap Y) = \mathrm{P}(X).\mathrm{P}(Y)$

28. Find the radius of gyration of the uniform rectangular lamina $PQRS$ about the edge PQ.

1 PQ is given

2 PS is given

29. Find the range of a projectile on the horizontal plane through its point of projection.

1 The height of the highest point above the point of projection is given

2 The time of flight is given

30. Show that the series $\sum_{n=1}^{\infty} u_n x^n$ is convergent,

1 $0 < x < 1$

2 $0 < u_n < \dfrac{1}{n}$ for all n

Test 10 (Further Mathematics)

Time allowed: 1 hour

The numerical value of g should be understood to be available for questions in any section if required. Take g as 10 ms^{-2} unless otherwise given.

SECTION I

Questions 1–10 **(Ten questions)**

1. $z = e^{i\theta}$, $\theta \in \mathbb{R}$.
$z^3 + z + z^{-1} + z^{-3} =$

A $\cos\theta + \cos 3\theta$

B $i\sin\theta + i\sin 3\theta$

C $2\cos\theta + 2\cos 3\theta$

D $2i\sin\theta + 2i\sin 3\theta$

E $2\cos\theta + 2\cos^3\theta$

2. The expansion of $e^x \sin x$ in ascending powers of x up to and including the term in x^3 is

A $1 + x - \dfrac{x^3}{3}$

B $1 + x + x^2 + \dfrac{2x^3}{3}$

C $x + x^2 + \dfrac{2x^3}{3}$

D $x + x^2 + \dfrac{x^3}{3}$

E $x + x^2 - \dfrac{x^3}{3}$

3. The complete set of real values of x for which $\cosh x > 2\sinh x$ is

A $\mathbb{R}^+$

B $\{x : x < \ln 3\}$

C $\{x : x < \frac{1}{2}\ln 3\}$

D $\mathbb{R}$

E $\{x : x < 0\}$

4. Air leaks from a spherical balloon at the constant rate of 2 m^3s^{-1}. When the radius of the balloon is 5 m, the rate, in m^2s^{-1}, at which the surface area is decreasing is

A $\dfrac{4}{5}$

B $\dfrac{8}{5}$

C $\dfrac{1}{50\pi}$

D $\dfrac{1}{100\pi}$

E none of the above

5. A sphere X, of mass m and moving with speed u, collides directly with a stationary sphere Y of mass λm. After impact, sphere X is at rest and sphere Y has speed v. The coefficient of restitution between the spheres is

A $v/(\lambda u)$

B $\lambda u/v$

C $\lambda v/u$

D u/v

E v/u

6. The graph of $y = \dfrac{x}{1 - x^2}$ could be

A

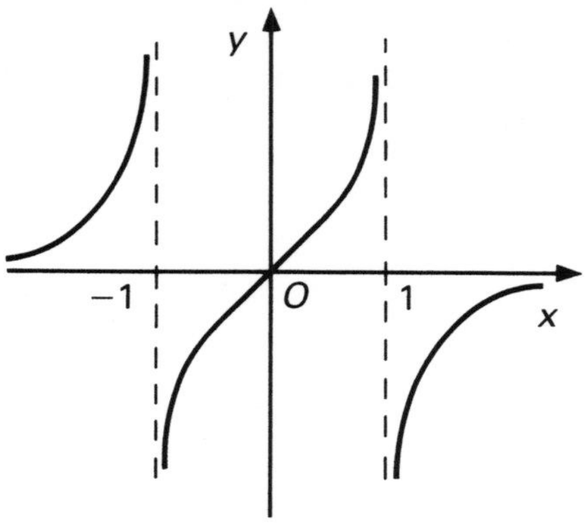

B

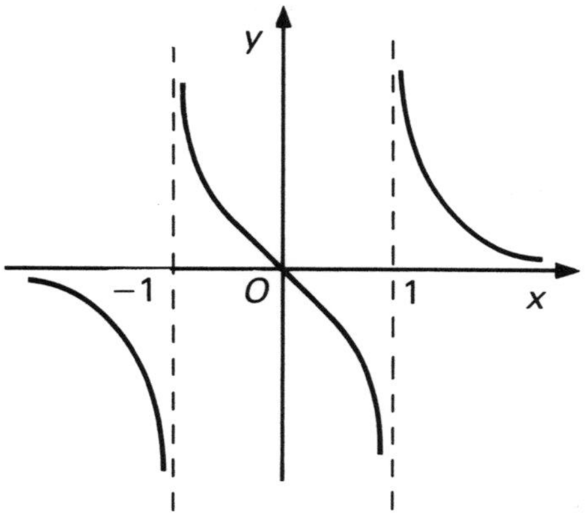

C

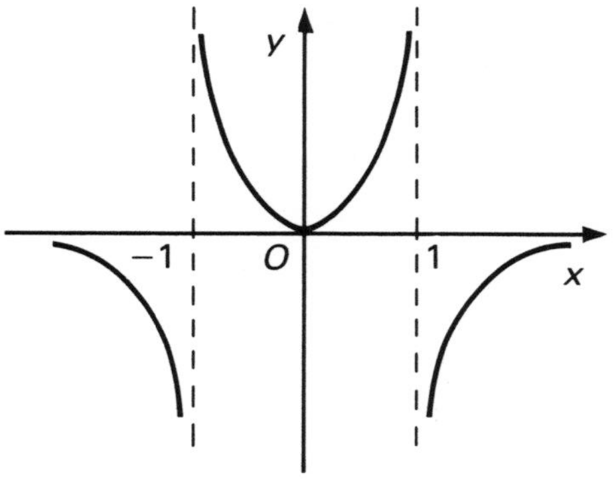

D

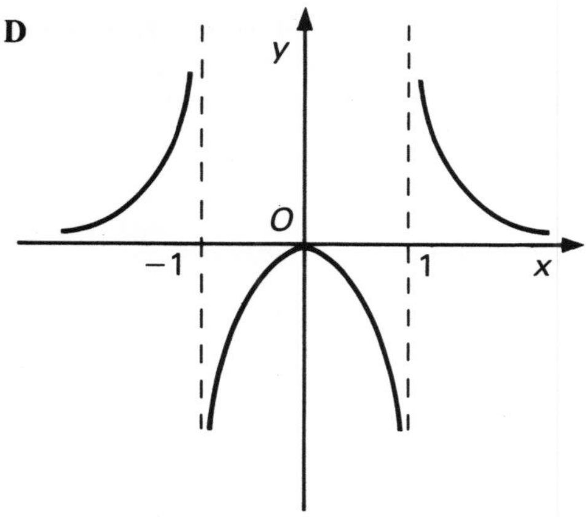

E

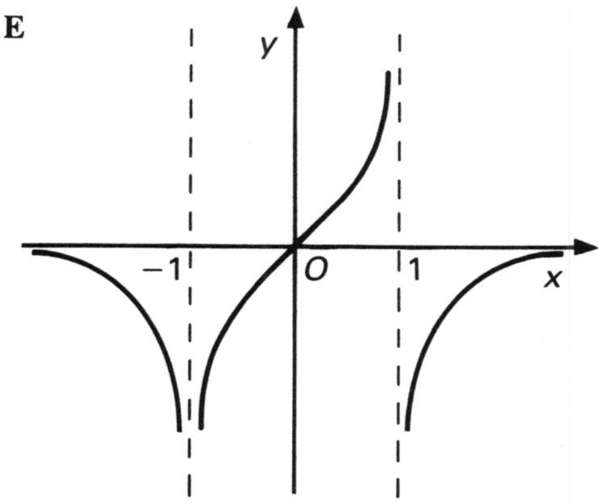

7. Forces 3**F**, − 2**F** act at the points with position vectors 2**a**, − **a** respectively, where **a**, **F** are non-zero vectors. The moment of the system about the origin is

A 4**a** . **F**

B 8**a** . **F**

C 8(**a** . **F**)**F**

D 4**a** × **F**

E 8**a** × **F**

8. $\displaystyle\int_0^{(\sqrt{3})/2} \frac{x}{\sqrt{(1 - x^2)}}\,dx =$

A $\dfrac{1}{4}$

B $\dfrac{1}{2}$

C 1

D $\pi/3$

E $-\dfrac{1}{2}$

9. At time t, the position vector $\mathbf{r}$ of a moving particle P, relative to a fixed point O in the plane of the motion, satisfies the equation

$$\frac{d^2\mathbf{r}}{dt^2} + n^2\mathbf{r} = \mathbf{0},$$

where n is a positive constant. At time $t = 0$,

$$\mathbf{r} = \mathbf{a}, \quad \frac{d\mathbf{r}}{dt} = \mathbf{v}.$$

Then $\mathbf{r} =$

A $\mathbf{a} \sin nt - (\mathbf{v}/n) \cos nt$

B $\mathbf{a} \cos nt + (\mathbf{v}/n) \sin nt$

C $\mathbf{a} \sinh nt + (\mathbf{v}/n) \cosh nt$

D $\mathbf{a} \cosh nt + (\mathbf{v}/n) \sinh nt$

E $\mathbf{a}\, e^{-nt} + (n\mathbf{a} + \mathbf{v})t\, e^{-nt}$

10. A lamina of mass M rotates with angular speed ω about an axis perpendicular to its plane. The moment of inertia of the lamina about the axis is I. Then the ratio of the kinetic energy of the lamina to the magnitude of the moment of momentum of the lamina about the axis

A is $I\omega : 2M$

B is $2M : I\omega$

C is $2 : \omega$

D is $\omega : 2$

E cannot be found from the given information

SECTION II

Questions 11–15 **(Five questions)**

11. For the curve $y = \dfrac{x^2}{x^2 + 3x + 2}$

1 the line $x = 2$ is an asymptote

2 the line $x = 1$ is an asymptote

3 the line $y = 1$ is an asymptote

12. Given that events X and Y are independent and $P(X) = 0{\cdot}2$, $P(Y) = 0{\cdot}3$, then

1 $P(X \cap Y) = 0{\cdot}06$

2 $P(X' \cap Y') = 0{\cdot}94$

3 $P(X \cup Y) = 0{\cdot}5$

13. $f : x \mapsto \ln x,\ x \in \mathbb{R}^+$.

1 $f(x) = \displaystyle\int_1^x \frac{1}{t}\, dt$

2 $f(x) < x$

3 $f^{-1} : x \mapsto e^x$

14. x and y are functions of t and dots denote differentiation with respect to t.

1 $\dfrac{dy}{dx} = \dfrac{\dot{y}}{\dot{x}}$

2 $\dfrac{dx}{dy} = \dfrac{\dot{x}}{\dot{y}}$

3 $\dfrac{d^2y}{dx^2} = \dfrac{\ddot{y}}{\ddot{x}}$

15. ω is a root of the equation
$$z^3 - 1 = 0$$
and Im $\omega \neq 0$.

1 $\omega^3 = \omega$

2 1 and ω^2 are the other two roots

3 $1 + \omega + \omega^2 = 0$

SECTION III

Questions 16–20 **(Five questions)**

16. **1** $\sinh(x/2) = 1$

2 $\cosh x = 3$

17. $a, b \in \mathbb{R}$ and $ab \neq 0$.

1 $a < b$

2 The series $\sum_{n=0}^{\infty} \left(\frac{a}{b}\right)^n$ converges

18. $\mathbf{a}$ is a non-zero vector and λ is a non-zero scalar.

1 $\mathbf{a} \times \mathbf{i} = \mathbf{0}$

2 $\mathbf{a} \times \mathbf{j} = \lambda\mathbf{k}, \mathbf{a} \times \mathbf{k} = -\lambda\mathbf{j}$

19. A particle moves along Ox in simple harmonic motion with amplitude a. The velocity at time t is v.

1 $|v| = \omega\sqrt{(a^2 - x^2)}$

2 The period of the motion is $2\pi/\omega$

20. $\frac{d^2y}{dx^2} + p\frac{dy}{dx} + qy = \cos x$, where p, q are real constants.

1 $p = -1, q = 1$

2 $\sin x$ is a particular integral

SECTION IV

Questions 21–25 **(Five questions)**

21. Using 2 strips and the trapezium rule for integration, estimate the value of

$$\int_{-h}^{h} f(x)\, dx.$$

1 $f(-h) + f(0)$ is given

2 $f(-h) + f(h)$ is given

3 $f(0) + f(h)$ is given

4 h is given

22. Given that a, b, c, k are constants, find the numerical value of the difference between the greatest and least values of the expression $ax^2 + bx + c$ in the interval $0 \leqslant x \leqslant k$.

1 a is given

2 b is given

3 c is given

4 k is given

23. A light spring, of natural length l and modulus λ, lies on a smooth horizontal table. One end of the spring is fixed and to the other end is attached a particle of mass m. The spring is compressed a distance a and then released. Find the time which elapses before the spring next has length l.

1 a is given

2 l is given

3 m is given

4 λ is given

24. A smooth elastic sphere, of mass m, is thrown vertically downwards with speed V from a point at a height h above a horizontal table. The coefficient of restitution between the sphere and the table is e. Find the magnitude of the impulse exerted by the plane on the sphere at the first impact.

1 m is given

2 V is given

3 h is given

4 e is given

25. Given that

$$u_n + au_{n-2} + b = 0$$

for $n \in \mathbb{N}$, $n \geqslant 2$, find the value of u_{10}.

1 a is given

2 b is given

3 u_0 is given

4 u_1 is given

SECTION V

Questions 26–30 **(Five questions)**

26. Show that the equation

$$\mathbf{r} = \mathbf{a} + s\mathbf{b} + t\mathbf{c},$$

where **a, b, c** are constant vectors and s, t are variable scalars, is the equation of a straight line.

1 $s = t$

2 $s = 1 - t$

27. Show that the curve $y = \mathrm{f}(x)$ has a point of inflexion at the point $[a, \mathrm{f}(a)]$.

1 $\mathrm{f}'(a) = 0$

2 $\mathrm{f}''(a) = 0$

28. Prove that $|x^2 - 5| > |x^2 - 3|$.

1 $x < 2$

2 $x > -2$

29. Prove that X and Y are independent events.

1 $\mathrm{P}(X \cap Y) = \mathrm{P}(X) \,.\, \mathrm{P}(Y)$

2 $\mathrm{P}(X \mid Y) = \mathrm{P}(X) \,.\, \mathrm{P}(Y)$

30. A uniform circular disc is free to rotate in a vertical plane about a smooth fixed horizontal axis which passes through a point on the circumference of the disc. Find the length of the equivalent simple pendulum.

1 The moment of inertia of the disc about the axis is given

2 The radius of the disc is given

Test 11 (Further Mathematics)

Time allowed: 1 hour

The numerical value of g should be understood to be available for questions in any section if required. Take g as 10 m s^{-2} unless otherwise given.

SECTION I

Questions 1–10 **(Ten questions)**

1. $e^{-2i\theta} =$

A $2\cos\theta - 2i\sin\theta$

B $\cos 2\theta - i\sin 2\theta$

C $-\cos 2\theta - i\sin 2\theta$

D $\cos 2\theta + i\sin 2\theta$

E $-2\cos\theta - 2i\sin\theta$

2. The matrix of a linear transformation of three-dimensional space is

$$\begin{pmatrix} 0 & 1 & 0 \\ 1 & 0 & 0 \\ 0 & 0 & 1 \end{pmatrix}$$

This transformation is a reflection in the plane

A $x = 0$

B $y = 0$

C $z = 0$

D $x + y = 0$

E $x - y = 0$

3. The number of asymptotes of the curve

$$y = \frac{x}{(x-1)(x-2)(x-3)}$$

is

A 4

B 3

C 2

D 1

E 0

4.

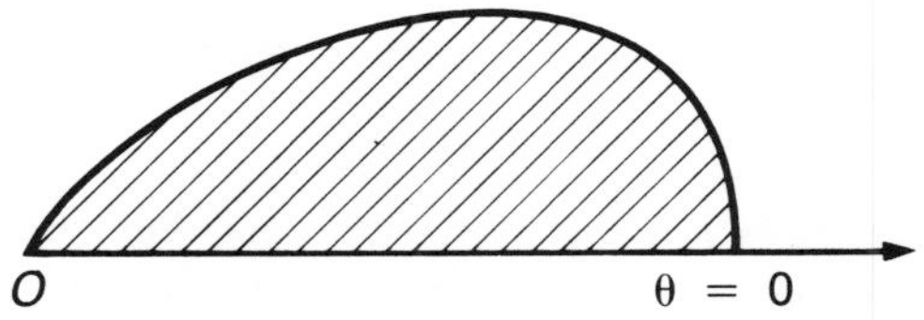

The diagram shows part of the curve whose equation in polar coordinates is $r = a\cos^2 2\theta$, where $a > 0$. The area of the shaded region is

A $\frac{1}{2}a^2 \int_0^{\pi/4} \cos^4 2\theta \, d\theta$

B $a^2 \int_0^{\pi/4} \cos^2 2\theta \, d\theta$

C $\frac{1}{2}a^2 \int_0^{\pi/4} \cos^2 2\theta \, d\theta$

D $a^2 \int_0^{\pi/4} \cos^2 2\theta \, d\theta$

E $\frac{1}{2}a^2 \int_{-\pi/4}^{\pi/4} \cos^4 2\theta \, d\theta$

5. A uniform rod OX, of mass $3m$ and length $2a$, has a particle of mass m fixed to it at X. The moment of inertia of the system about an axis which passes through O and is perpendicular to OX is λma^2, where $\lambda =$

A 2

B 7/3

C 16/3

D 5

E 8

6. Forces **F** and −**F** act at the points with position vectors **a** and −**a** respectively, where **F** and **a** are non-zero. The system

A is in equilibrium

B is equivalent to a force 2**F** acting through the origin

C is equivalent to a couple of moment 2**a** × **F**

D is equivalent to a couple of moment **a** × **F**

E is equivalent to a couple of moment 2**F** × **a**

7. A particle moving along Ox describes simple harmonic motion. It makes 8 complete oscillations in one second and its greatest speed is 0·1 m s^{-1}. The greatest magnitude of its acceleration, in m s^{-2}, is

A 8/5

B 8π/5

C 4π/5

D π/4

E π/40

8. A uniform circular disc, of mass m and radius a, rotates about a fixed axis l which passes through the rim of the disc and is perpendicular to its plane. The speed of the centre of the disc is V. Then the magnitude of the moment of momentum of the disc about l is

A $3mV^2/4$

B $5mV^2/4$

C maV

D $5maV/4$

E none of the above

9. The probability that Wendy will win a single game of tennis when playing against Karen is constant and equals $\frac{2}{5}$. The probability that Wendy will win at least 5 games out of 6 is

A $\left(\frac{2}{5}\right)^6$

B $9\left(\frac{2}{5}\right)^6$

C $10\left(\frac{2}{5}\right)^6$

D $4\left(\frac{3}{5}\right)^6$

E $5\left(\frac{3}{5}\right)^6$

10. An equation of a line is

$$\mathbf{r} = \mathbf{a} + t\mathbf{b},$$

where **a, b** are non-zero vectors and t is a variable scalar. The value of t which gives the point on the line nearest to the origin is

A 0

B −**a**/**b**

C (**a** . **b**)/(**b** . **b**)

D −(**a** . **b**)/(**b** . **b**)

E −(**b** . **b**)/(**a** . **b**)

SECTION II

Questions 11–15 **(Five questions)**

11. ω is a root of the equation $z^3 - 1 = 0$, and $\text{Im}\,\omega \neq 0$.

1 $1 + \omega + \omega^2 = 0$

2 $1 + \dfrac{1}{\omega} + \dfrac{1}{\omega^2} = 0$

3 $1 + \omega^3 + \omega^6 = 0$

12. The n-th term of an infinite series is x^n/n.

1 The series converges when $x = 1$

2 The series converges when $x = -1$

3 When $x = -\frac{1}{2}$, the series converges to $-\ln(3/2)$

13. $x = e^t$ and y is a function of x.

1 $\dfrac{dx}{dt} = x$

2 $x\dfrac{dy}{dx} = \dfrac{dy}{dt}$

3 $x^2\dfrac{d^2y}{dx^2} = \dfrac{d^2y}{dt^2}$

14. $x \in \mathbb{Z}^+, x \neq 2$.
p denotes the statement 'x is prime'.
q denotes the statement 'x^2 is odd'.

1 $p \Rightarrow q$

2 $q \Rightarrow p$

3 $\sim p \Rightarrow \sim q$

15.

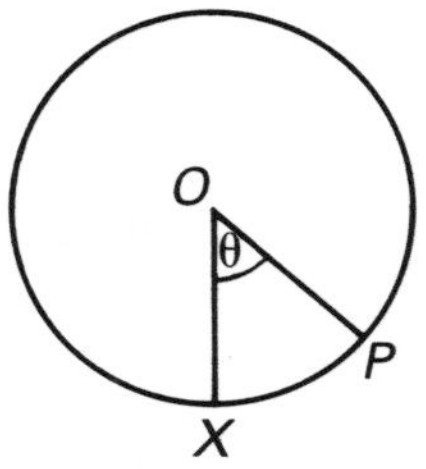

A particle P, free to move on the smooth inner surface of a fixed hollow sphere of centre O and internal radius a, is given a horizontal velocity of magnitude $\sqrt{(2ga)}$ when it is at the lowest point X of the sphere.
When angle $XOP = \theta$,

1 the speed of P is $\sqrt{(2ga \cos \theta)}$

2 $a\ddot{\theta} = - g \sin \theta$

3 the force exerted by the sphere on P is of magnitude $3mg \cos \theta$

SECTION III

Questions 16–20 **(Five questions)**

16. The cubic equation $f(z) = 0$ has real coefficients.

1 $2 - 3i$ is a root

2 $-2 + 3i$ is a root

17. $f(x)$ is a continuous function.

1 $f(-x) = f(x)$

2 $\displaystyle\int_{-1}^{1} f(x)\,dx = 2\int_{0}^{1} f(x)\,dx$

18. 1 $\sin x = \dfrac{1}{2}$

2 $\cos x = \dfrac{\sqrt{3}}{2}$

19. 1 The resultant force acting on the particle P is a non-zero constant

2 The particle P moves with constant velocity

20. **a** and **b** are non-parallel non-zero vectors.

1 $|\mathbf{a}| = |\mathbf{b}|$

2 $(\mathbf{a} - \mathbf{b})$ is perpendicular to $(\mathbf{a} + \mathbf{b})$

SECTION IV

Questions 21–25 **(Five questions)**

21. A rigid lamina, with centre of mass G, rotates about a fixed axis OX which is perpendicular to its plane. The line GY is parallel to OX. Calculate the kinetic energy of the lamina.

1 The angular speed of the lamina is given

2 The mass of the lamina is given

3 The distance between OX and GY is given

4 The moment of inertia of the lamina about GY is given

22. Two particles P_1 and P_2 moving with constant velocities $\mathbf{v}_1$ and $\mathbf{v}_2$ respectively, collide directly and coalesce. Find the velocity of the composite particle after the collision.

1 $\mathbf{v}_1$ is given

2 $\mathbf{v}_1 - \mathbf{v}_2$ is given

3 The mass of P_1 is given

4 The mass of P_1 is equal to the mass of P_2.

23. Find the coefficient of x^6 in the expansion, in ascending powers of x,

$$\ln [(1 + ax)/(1 + bx)] + \sin cx + e^{dx},$$

where a, b, c, d are constants.

1 a is given

2 b is given

3 c is given

4 d is given

24.

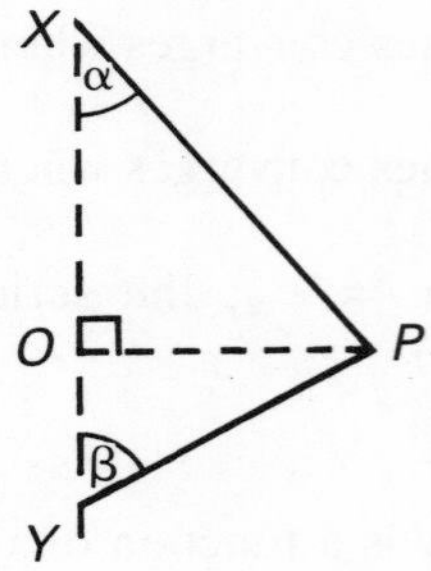

A smooth ring P is threaded on a light inextensible string. The ends of the string are attached to fixed points X and Y in the same vertical line and the system rotates with constant angular speed ω so that P moves in a horizontal circle with centre O. Calculate ω.

1 The tension in the string is given

2 α is given

3 β is given

4 The length XP is given

25. The force $(p\mathbf{i} + q\mathbf{j})$ N acts at the point with position vector $r\mathbf{i}$ m and the force $(p\mathbf{i} - q\mathbf{j})$ N acts at the point with position vector $(r\mathbf{i} + s\mathbf{k})$ m. Find the total moment of these two forces about the origin.

1 p is given

2 q is given

3 r is given

4 s is given

SECTION V

Questions 26–30 **(Five questions)**

26. Prove that at least one of the vectors **p, q** is a null vector.

1 $\mathbf{p} \times \mathbf{q} = \mathbf{0}$

2 $\mathbf{p} \cdot \mathbf{q} = 0$

27. Show that the infinite series $\sum_{n=1}^{\infty} u_n x^n$ converges.

1 $|x| < 1$

2 $|u_n| < 1$

28. Find whether the series $\sum_{n=1}^{\infty} \frac{x^n}{n}$ converges.

1 $x \leqslant 1$

2 $x \geqslant -1$

29. Two particles P and Q, of masses 0·1 kg and 0·2 kg respectively, are attached to the ends of a light inextensible string and rest on a smooth horizontal table with the string taut. A force, of magnitude F N, acts on P in the direction of $\overrightarrow{QP}$. Calculate the tension in the string PQ.

1 The acceleration of P is given

2 F is given

30. Find the constants p, q, r in the differential equation

$$p\frac{d^2y}{dx^2} + q\frac{dy}{dx} + y = x + r.$$

1 The complementary function is of the form $Pe^x + Qe^{-x/2}$, P and Q being arbitrary constants

2 A particular integral is $x - 1$

Test 12 (Further Mathematics)

Time allowed: 1 hour

The numerical value of g should be understood to be available for questions in any section if required. Take g as 10 m s^{-2} unless otherwise given.

SECTION I

Questions 1–10 **(Ten questions)**

1. The moment of inertia of a uniform circular disc, of mass m and radius a, about the line l, which is perpendicular to the disc and which passes through its circumference, is

A $5ma^2/4$

B $4ma^2/3$

C $3ma^2/2$

D $2ma^2$

E $7ma^2/3$

2. $\int \frac{1}{\sqrt{(9 + 4x^2)}} dx =$

A $\tan^{-1}\left(\frac{2x}{3}\right)$ + constant

B $\frac{1}{6}\tan^{-1}\left(\frac{2x}{3}\right)$ + constant

C $\sinh^{-1}\left(\frac{2x}{3}\right)$ + constant

D $\frac{1}{2}\sinh^{-1}\left(\frac{2x}{3}\right)$ + constant

E $\frac{1}{3}\sinh^{-1}\left(\frac{3x}{2}\right)$ + constant

3. The force **F**, where **F** = (6**i** + 4**j** + 5**k**)N, acts at the point with position vector (4**i** + 2**j** + 3**k**)m. The moment, in Nm, of **F** about the point with position vector (− 3**i** + 7**j** + **k**)m is

A 33**i** + 23**j** − 58**k**

B − 33**i** − 23**j** + 58**k**

C 2**i** + 2**j** − 4**k**

D − 2**i** − 2**j** + 4**k**

E 42**i** − 20**j** + 10**k**

4. The number of positive roots of the equation $\tanh x = x$ is

A 0

B 1

C 2

D 3

E more than 4

5. $z = 2\left(\cos\frac{\pi}{3} - i\sin\frac{\pi}{3}\right)$.

$z + \frac{1}{z} =$

A 2

B $\sqrt{3}$

C $\frac{1}{4}(3 - 5\sqrt{3}\,i)$

D $\frac{1}{2}(5 - 3\sqrt{3}\,i)$

E $\frac{1}{4}(5 - 3\sqrt{3}\,i)$

6. The graph of $y = \ln(1 - x^2)$ could be

A

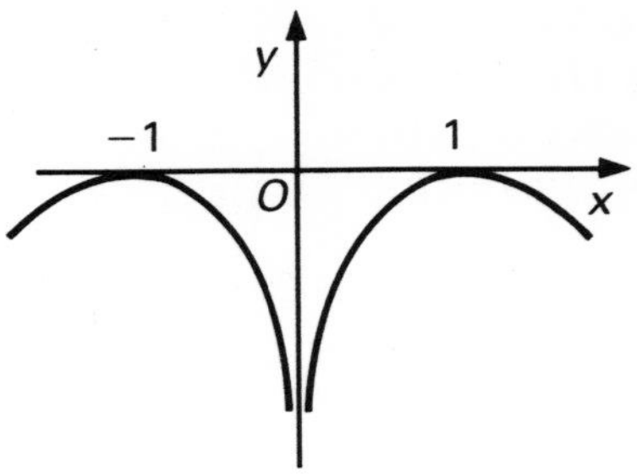

B

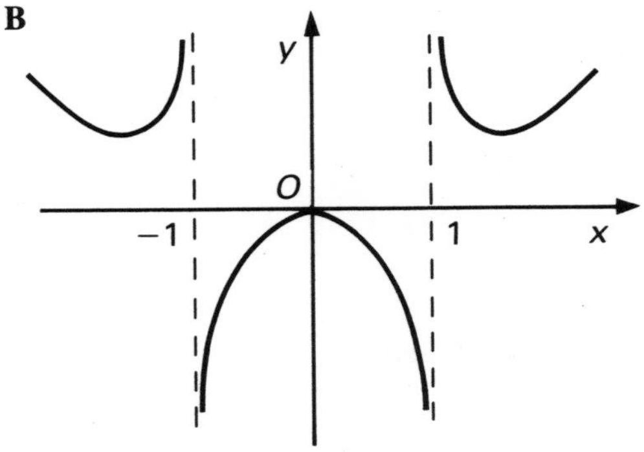

C

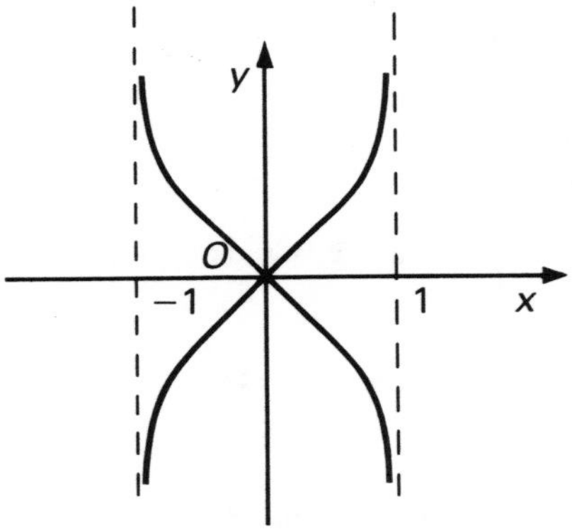

D

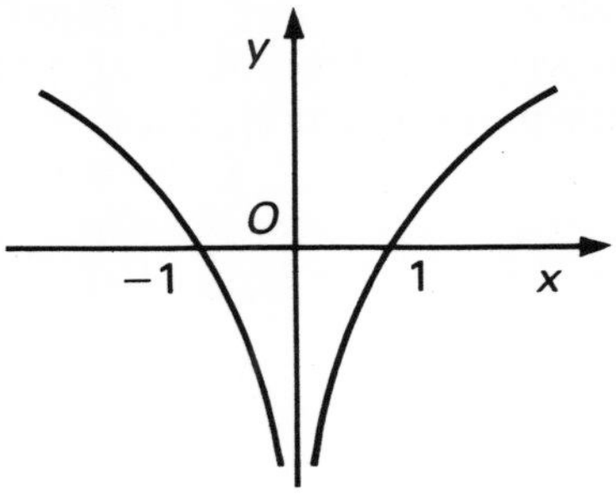

E

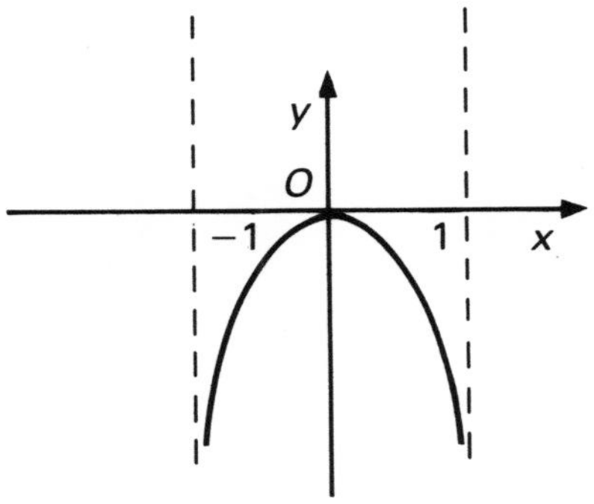

7. An integrating factor for the differential equation

$$\frac{dy}{dx} + (1 + x)y = x^2$$

is

A $e^{x^3/3}$

B $e^{(1+x)^2/2}$

C $\dfrac{1}{1 + x}$

D $x\,e^{-1/x}$

E $1 + x$

8.

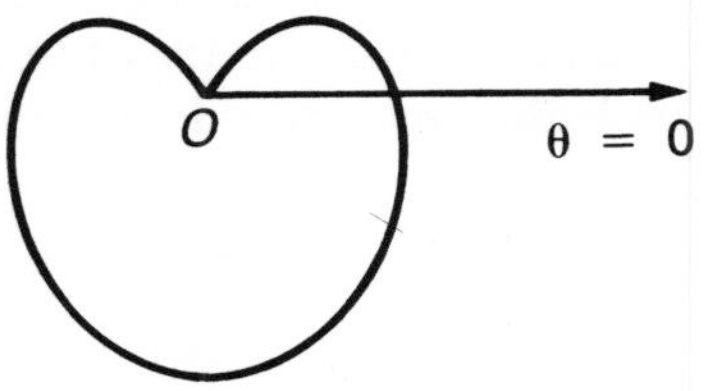

The diagram could be a sketch of the curve with equation, in polar form,

A $r = 1 + \cos\theta$

B $r = 1 - \cos\theta$

C $r = 1 + \sin\theta$

D $r = 1 - \sin\theta$

E $r = \cos^2\theta$

9. A particle P is projected with speed 40 ms^{-1} at an angle of elevation $\tan^{-1}(\frac{3}{4})$. After 2 seconds, P is moving in a direction making the angle θ with the upward vertical. Then $\tan \theta =$

A 8

B 2

C $\dfrac{1}{2}$

D $\dfrac{1}{8}$

E none of these

10. In an experiment the constant probability that a trial will be successful is p. Three trials are to be made. The probability that not more than one will be successful is

A $(1 - p)^3$

B $3p(1 - p)^2$

C $(1 - p)^2 (1 + 2p)$

D $p^2(3 - 2p)$

E p^3

SECTION II

Questions 11–15 **(Five questions)**

11. $x, y, n \in \mathbb{R}^+$.

1 $\displaystyle\int_1^{xy} \frac{1}{t}\, dt = \int_1^{x} \frac{1}{t}\, dt + \int_1^{y} \frac{1}{t}\, dt$

2 $\displaystyle\int_1^{x^n} \frac{1}{t}\, dt = n \int_1^{x} \frac{1}{t}\, dt$

3 $\displaystyle\int_1^{x/y} \frac{1}{t}\, dt = \int_1^{x} \frac{1}{t}\, dt - \int_1^{y} \frac{1}{t}\, dt$

12. A particle P of mass 1 kg moves along Ox and performs simple harmonic motion of amplitude 4 m under the action of a force of magnitude $9\,|x|$ N directed towards the origin O.

1 The period is $2\pi/3$ s

2 The maximum speed of P is 12 m s^{-1}

3 The greatest value of the magnitude of the acceleration of P is 48 m s^{-2}

13. $\displaystyle I = \int_0^{\pi/2} \sin^6 x \, dx, \qquad J = \int_0^{\pi/2} \cos^6 x \, dx.$

1 $J > I$

2 $\displaystyle\int_0^{\pi/2} \sin^6 x \cos^6 x \, dx = IJ$

3 $\displaystyle\int_0^{2\pi} \sin^6 x \, dx = 4I$

14. Two smooth spheres, of equal radii but unequal mass, collide.

1 The total linear momentum is conserved

2 The heavier sphere must lose kinetic energy

3 The lighter sphere must gain kinetic energy

15. **a** and **b** are non-zero, non-parallel vectors.

1 **a** /|**a**| is a unit vector in the direction of **a**

2 (**a** × **b**)/ |**a** × **b**| is a unit vector perpendicular to **a**

3 (**a** . **b**) **b**/(**b** . **b**) is the component of **a** in the direction of **b**

SECTION III

Questions 16–20 **(Five questions)**

16. z_1 and z_2 are non-zero complex numbers.

1 $z_1 = z_2^*$

2 $z_1 z_2$ is real

17. x and $y \in \mathbb{R}$, and $xy \neq 0$.

1 $|x| < |y|$

2 $\frac{1}{x} < \frac{1}{y}$

18. **X** and **Y** are $n \times n$ matrices and **O** is the $n \times n$ null matrix.

1 $\mathbf{XY} - \mathbf{YX} = \mathbf{O}$

2 $\mathbf{X} = \mathbf{O}$ or $\mathbf{Y} = \mathbf{O}$

19. For the differential equation

$$\frac{d^2y}{dx^2} + p\frac{dy}{dx} + qy = 0,$$

where $p, q \in \mathbb{R}$,

1 a general solution is $Pe^{\alpha x} + Qe^{\beta x}$, where $\alpha, \beta \in \mathbb{R}$, P and Q are arbitrary constants and $\alpha \neq \beta$.

2 $p^2 > 4q$

20. The equation of motion of a particle moving along Ox is

$$\frac{d^2x}{dt^2} + kx = 0,$$

where k is a real constant.

1 $k > 0$

2 The motion is simple harmonic

SECTION IV

Questions 21–25 **(Five questions)**

21. A boy is to be chosen at random from a class of boys. Find the probability that the boy chosen plays rugby.

1 The number who play neither rugby nor soccer is given

2 The number who play rugby but not soccer is given

3 The number who play soccer but not rugby is given

4 The number who play both soccer and rugby is given

22. Two beads P and Q, of masses m and λm respectively, are threaded on a fixed horizontal smooth thin circular wire of radius a. The coefficient of restitution between the beads is e. Bead P is projected along the wire with speed v. Find the time which elapses between the first and second collisions between P and Q.

1 a is given

2 e is given

3 λ is given

4 v is given

23. α, β, γ are the roots of the equation

$$ax^3 + bx^2 + cx + d = 0,$$

where a, b, c, d are constants and $a \neq 0$. Find the value of $\alpha^2 + \beta^2 + \gamma^2$.

1 a is given

2 b is given

3 c is given

4 d is given

24. A compound pendulum consists of a rod AB free to move in a vertical plane with a particle attached rigidly to the end B. Find the period of small oscillations under gravity about a smooth horizontal axis which passes through A.

1 The mass of the rod is given

2 The mass of the particle is given

3 The length of the rod is given

4 The rod is uniform

25.

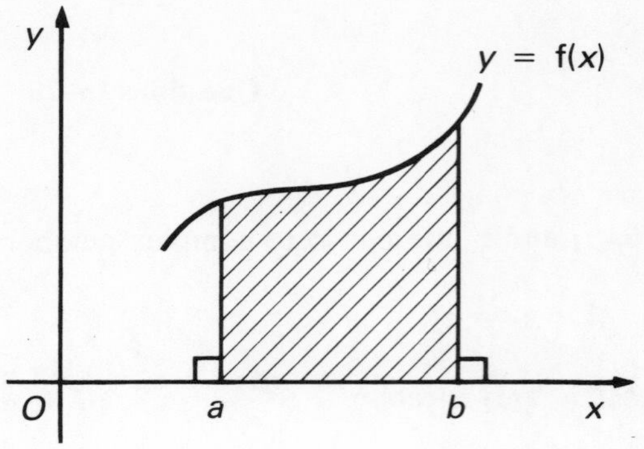

Find the coordinates of the centroid of the shaded region.

1 $\int_a^b [f(x)]^2 dx$ is given

2 $\int_a^b x[(f(x)]^2 dx$ is given

3 $\int_a^b x f(x)\, dx$ is given

4 $\int_a^b f(x) dx$ is given

SECTION V

Questions 26–30 **(Five questions)**

26. Prove that the equation

$$z^3 + az^2 + bz + c = 0,$$

where $a, b, c \in \mathbb{R}$, has only one real root.

1 $a = 0$

2 $b > 0$

27. Show that the series $\sum_{n=1}^{\infty} u_n x^n$ is convergent.

1 $u_n = \dfrac{1}{n!}$ for $n \in \mathbb{N}$

2 $|x| < 1$

28.

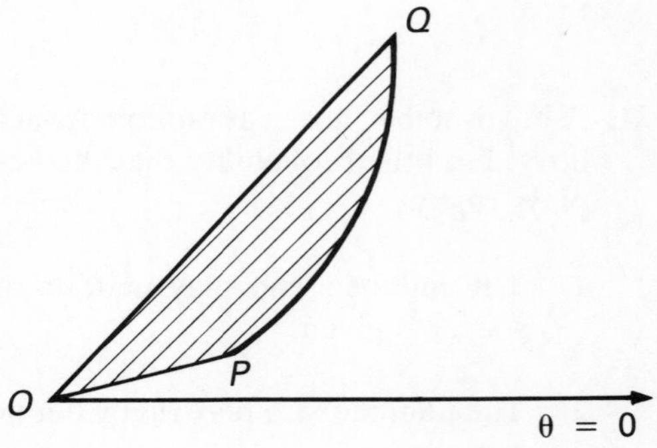

PQ is an arc of the curve $r = e^{2\theta}$. Calculate the area of the shaded sector.

1 The angle POQ is given

2 The lengths of OP and OQ are given

29. The position vector of a point on the line of action of the force $\mathbf{F}_m$ is $\mathbf{r}_m$, $m = 1, 2, \ldots, n$. Show that the system of n forces is in equilibrium.

1 $\sum_{m=1}^{n} \mathbf{F}_m = \mathbf{0}$

2 $\sum_{m=1}^{n} \mathbf{r}_m = \mathbf{0}$

30. A game is to be played between three players, Alice, Eva and Jean, in which each player throws an unbiased coin in turn, the winner being the player who first throws a tail. Find the probability that Eva wins.

1 Alice throws first

2 Eva throws second

Test 13 (Applied Mathematics)

Time allowed: 1 hour

The numerical value of g should be understood to be available for questions in any section if required. Take g as 10 m s^{-2} unless otherwise given.

SECTION I

Questions 1–10 **(Ten questions)**

1. A wheel makes 300 revolutions per minute. The angular speed, in rad s^{-1}, is

A 600π

B 10π

C 5π

D $2\pi/5$

E $5/(2\pi)$

2.

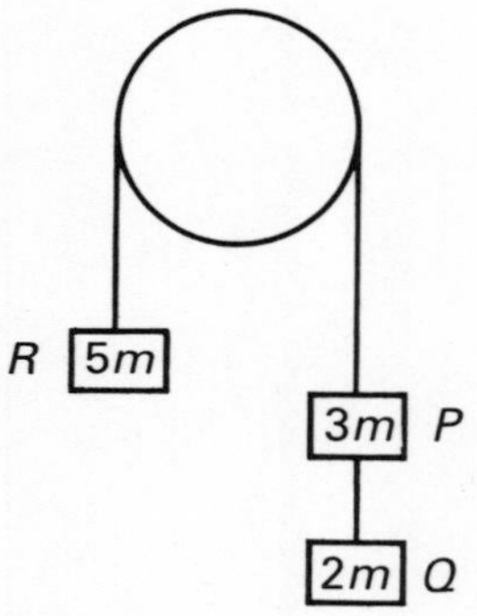

The system shown rests in equilibrium with the string passing over a smooth pulley. The other parts of the strings are vertical. When the string connecting P and Q is cut, the acceleration of R is of magnitude

A $g/4$

B g

C $15g/4$

D $4g$

E none of these

3. Which one of the following is not a vector quantity?

A force

B acceleration

C momentum

D moment of momentum

E kinetic energy

4.

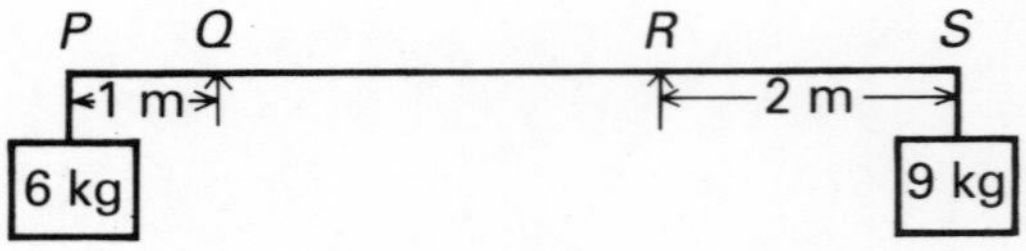

$PQRS$ is a uniform beam, of mass 15 kg and length 6 m, supported on knife edges at Q and R, where PQ = 1 m, RS = 2 m. Loads of masses 6 kg and 9 kg are hung from P and S respectively. The magnitude of the force, in N, exerted on the support at R is

A 23

B 70

C 30

D 230

E 270

5. A ship is steaming due north with speed 10 km h^{-1} and collides with another ship steaming due east at 24 km h^{-1}. Twelve minutes before the collision the distance, in km, between the ships is

A 2·6

B 2·8

C 5·2

D 18·72

E 26

6. The position vectors of P, Q, relative to the origin O, are $(-\mathbf{i} + \mathbf{j} - \mathbf{k})$, $(\mathbf{i} - 2\mathbf{j} + \mathbf{k})$ respectively. A unit vector perpendicular to the plane OPQ is

A $\frac{1}{\sqrt{17}}(2\mathbf{i} - 3\mathbf{j} + 2\mathbf{k})$

B $\frac{1}{\sqrt{10}}(3\mathbf{i} + \mathbf{k})$

C $\frac{1}{\sqrt{6}}(-\mathbf{i} - 2\mathbf{j} + \mathbf{k})$

D $\frac{1}{\sqrt{2}}(-\mathbf{i} + \mathbf{k})$

E none of the above

7. A particle P, of mass m, moves along Ox under the action of a force of magnitude $mn^2|x|$ directed towards O and a resistance of magnitude $2mkv$, where v is the speed of P and n, k are positive constants. An equation of motion is

A $\ddot{x} = -n^2x - 2k\dot{x}$

B $\ddot{x} = -n^2x + 2k\dot{x}$

C $\ddot{x} = n^2x + 2k\dot{x}$

D $\ddot{x} = n^2x - 2k\dot{x}$

E $\frac{dv}{dx} = -n^2x - 2k\dot{x}$

8. X and Y are mutually exclusive events such that $P(X) = P(Y')$. Then $P(X \cup Y) =$

A $P(X) \,.\, P(Y)$

B $P(X)$

C $P(Y)$

D 0

E 1

9. The force $\mathbf{F}$ acts through the point with position vector $\mathbf{r}_1$. The moment of $\mathbf{F}$ about the point with position vector $\mathbf{r}_2$ is

A $(\mathbf{r}_2 - \mathbf{r}_1) \,.\, \mathbf{F}$

B $(\mathbf{r}_1 - \mathbf{r}_2) \,.\, \mathbf{F}$

C $(\mathbf{r}_1 - \mathbf{r}_2) \times \mathbf{F}$

D $(\mathbf{r}_2 - \mathbf{r}_1) \times \mathbf{F}$

E $\mathbf{F} \times (\mathbf{r}_1 - \mathbf{r}_2)$

10. A uniform rod PQ, of length $2a$, is free to rotate in a vertical plane about a smooth horizontal axis through the end P. The rod is released from rest with PQ horizontal. When Q is vertically below P, the angular speed of the rod is

A $\sqrt{[3g/(4a)]}$

B $\sqrt{[3g/(2a)]}$

C $\sqrt{(2g/a)}$

D $\sqrt{(3ga/2)}$

E $\sqrt{(2ag)}$

SECTION II

Questions 11–15 **(Five questions)**

11. A ball is projected horizontally with speed 15 m s^{-1} from the top of a tower of height 20 m and lands on the horizontal plane through the foot of the tower.

1 The time of flight is 2 s

2 The distance of the landing point from the foot of the tower is 30 m

3 The angle which the velocity of the ball makes with the horizontal when it strikes the plane is $\tan^{-1}(\frac{1}{2})$

12. Two equal smooth perfectly elastic spheres collide directly.

1 The total momentum of the spheres is unaltered by the collision

2 The total kinetic energy of the spheres is unaltered by the collision

3 The relative velocity of the spheres is unaltered by the collision

13. A particle describes simple harmonic motion along Ox about O as centre and is instantaneously at rest at P and Q, where $PQ = 2a$. At O its speed is ka.

1 The acceleration of the particle at O is zero

2 The acceleration of the particle at P is of magnitude $2k^2a$

3 The time to travel once from P to Q is $2\pi/k$

14. $\frac{d\mathbf{r}}{dt} + k\mathbf{r} = \mathbf{0}$, where $k > 0$ and $\mathbf{r} \neq \mathbf{0}$.

1 $\frac{d^2\mathbf{r}}{dt^2} = k^2\mathbf{r}$

2 $\mathbf{r} \times \frac{d\mathbf{r}}{dt} = \mathbf{0}$

3 $\mathbf{r} \cdot \frac{d\mathbf{r}}{dt} < 0$

15. The position vector of P is $(\mathbf{i} - 2\mathbf{j} + \mathbf{k})$ m. A force $\mathbf{F}$, where $\mathbf{F} = (3\mathbf{i} + \mathbf{j} + 2\mathbf{k})$N, acts through P.

1 $|\mathbf{F}| = 6$ N

2 The moment of $\mathbf{F}$ about O is 3 Nm

3 An equation of the line of action of $\mathbf{F}$ is $\mathbf{r} = (\mathbf{i} - 2\mathbf{j} + \mathbf{k}) + t(3\mathbf{i} + \mathbf{j} + 2\mathbf{k})$

SECTION III

Questions 16–20 **(Five questions)**

16. A particle is projected from a point of a horizontal plane with speed 40 m s^{-1}.

1 The angle of projection from the horizontal is 30°

2 The range of the particle on the plane is 40 m

17. A particle is free to move on the inside of a smooth fixed hollow sphere, of internal radius a and centre O. The particle moves in a vertical plane passing through O.

1 The maximum speed of the particle exceeds $\sqrt{(2ga)}$

2 The particle makes complete circles

18. **a** and **b** are non-zero, non-parallel vectors, and $r \neq \mathbf{0}$.

1 $\mathbf{x} = \mathbf{a} + \mathbf{b}$

2 $\mathbf{r} \times \mathbf{x} = \mathbf{r} \times \mathbf{a} + \mathbf{r} \times \mathbf{b}$

19. X and Y are events in a finite sample space.

1 $P(X \cap Y) = 0$

2 Events X and Y are mutually exclusive

20. A non-uniform rod PQ, of mass m and length $2a$, is free to rotate in a vertical plane about a smooth horizontal axis through P.

1 The centre of mass of the rod is at G, where $PG = a/2$

2 The moment of inertia of the rod about the axis is $ma^2/4$

SECTION IV

Questions 21–25 **(Five questions)**

21.

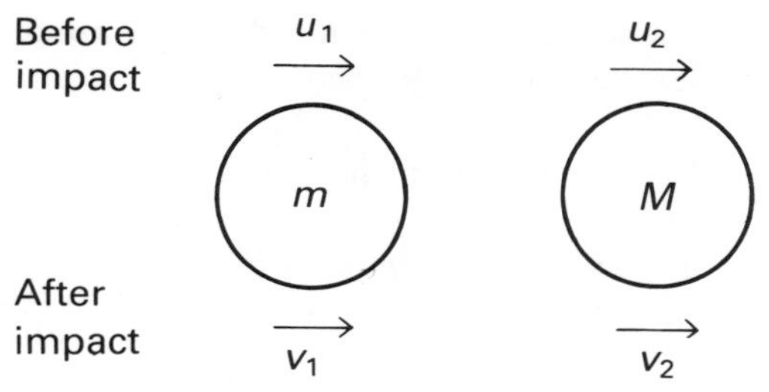

The spheres shown collide directly. Calculate the coefficient of restitution between the spheres.

1 The ratio m/M is given

2 The value of u_1 is given

3 The value of u_2 is given

4 The value of $v_2 - v_1$ is given

22. A train moves along a straight horizontal track against a constant frictional resistance. Find its acceleration.

1 The speed of the train is given

2 The mass of the train is given

3 The rate of working of the engine is given

4 The constant frictional resistance is given

23.

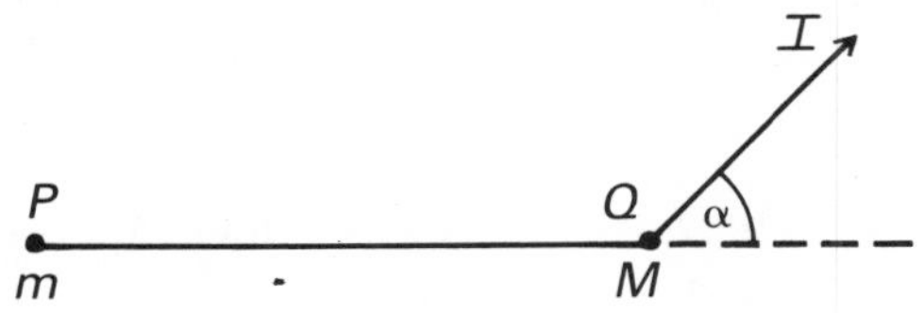

Two particles P and Q, of masses m and M respectively, are connected by a light rigid rod and rest on a smooth horizontal table as shown. A horizontal impulse, of magnitude I and acting in a direction making the angle α with PQ produced, is applied to Q. Find the component of the velocity of Q perpendicular to the rod.

1 M is given

2 m is given

3 α is given

4 I is given

24. *Ox, Oy, Oz* are mutually perpendicular axes. Find the moment of inertia of a lamina about *Ox*.

1 The moment of inertia of the lamina about *Oy* is given

2 The moment of inertia of the lamina about *Oz* is given

3 *O* is the centre of mass of the lamina

4 The lamina lies in the plane $x = 0$

25. A particle *P* moves along *Ox* and the only force acting on it is a resisting force of magnitude $(a + bv)$N per unit mass, where a and b are constants and v is the speed of *P* at time t. Find v when $t = 2$ s.

1 When $t = 0$, v is given

2 When $t = 0$, the retardation is given

3 a is given

4 When $t = 0$, *P* is at *O*.

SECTION V

Questions 26–30 **(Five questions)**

26. A particle *P*, of mass 0 · 1 kg, moves under the action of a single force **F**. Find the acceleration of *P*.

1 The rate of change of momentum of *P* is given

2 The magnitude of **F** is given

27. *X* and *Y* are events. Find $P(X \cup Y)$.

1 $P(X) = \frac{1}{4} = P(Y)$

2 $P(X \cap Y) = \frac{1}{12}$

28. A rod *PQ* is rotating in a horizontal plane with angular speed ω about a smooth fixed pivot at *P*. Calculate ω.

1 The kinetic energy of the rod is given

2 The moment of momentum of the rod about *P* is given

29. A particle is projected from a point on a horizontal plane. Find the maximum height reached above the plane.

1 The range on the plane is given

2 The time of flight is given

30. A system of forces acts in the plane of the triangle *OPQ*, where *OP* = 30 cm, *OQ* = 40 cm and *PQ* = 50 cm. Find the magnitude of the resultant of this system.

1 The moment of the system about *P* is given

2 The moment of the system about *Q* is given

Test 14 (Applied Mathematics)

Time allowed: 1 hour

The numerical value of g should be understood to be available for questions in any section if required. Take g as 10 m s^{-2} unless otherwise given.

SECTION I

Questions 1–10 **(Ten questions)**

1.

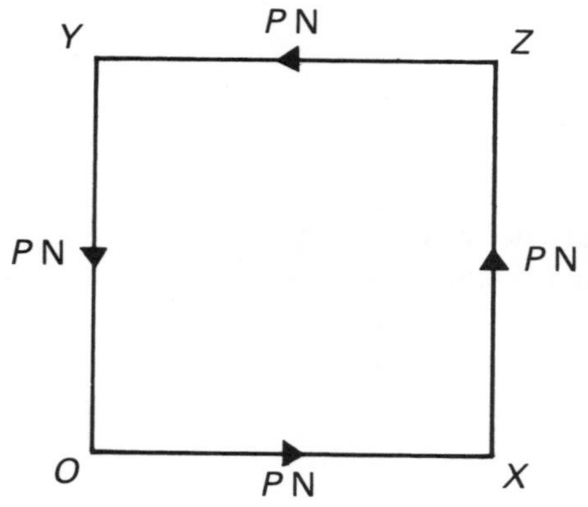

Four non-zero forces of equal magnitude act as shown round the sides of a square $OXZY$. This system

A is in equilibrium

B is equivalent to a force acting through O

C is equivalent to a force acting through X

D is equivalent to a force acting through the mid-point of OZ

E is equivalent to a couple

2. A parcel, of mass m, is on the floor of a lift. At the instant when the lift is moving downwards with speed v and accelerating upwards with acceleration f, the upward force exerted by the floor of the lift on the parcel is of magnitude

A $m(g + f)$

B $m(g - f)$

C $mv(g + f)$

D $mv(g - f)$

E mfv

3. The moment of inertia of a thin uniform circular hoop, of radius a and mass m, about an axis in its plane tangential to the hoop is

A $2ma^2$

B $3ma^2/2$

C ma^2

D $3ma^2/4$

E $ma^2/2$

4. A point P is chosen at random within the circle $x^2 + y^2 = 4a^2$, where $a > 0$. The probability that P will lie outside the square for which $|x| \leqslant a$, $|y| \leqslant a$ is

A 0

B $\frac{1}{\pi}$

C $1 - \frac{1}{\pi}$

D $1 - \frac{1}{4\pi}$

E none of the above

5.

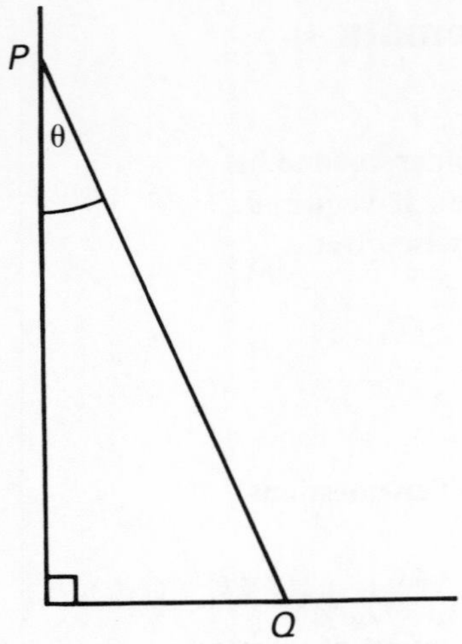

The uniform rod PQ, of weight W, rests in non-limiting equilibrium with its end Q on rough horizontal ground, coefficient of friction μ, and its end P against a smooth vertical wall. The vertical plane through the rod is perpendicular to the wall. The force of friction between the rod and the ground is of magnitude

A μW

B $\frac{1}{2}\mu W$

C $W \tan \theta$

D $\frac{1}{2}W \tan \theta$

E $\frac{1}{2}W \cot \theta$

6. Given that

$$\frac{d^2\mathbf{r}}{dt^2} + 2k\frac{d\mathbf{r}}{dt} + (k^2 + n^2)\mathbf{r} = \mathbf{0},$$

where k and n are positive constants, then, **P** and **Q** being constant arbitrary vectors,
$\mathbf{r}$ =

A $e^{nt}(\mathbf{P} \cos kt + \mathbf{Q} \sin kt)$

B $e^{-kt}(\mathbf{P} \cos nt + \mathbf{Q} \sin nt)$

C $e^{-nt}(\mathbf{P} \cos kt + \mathbf{Q} \sin kt)$

D $e^{kt}(\mathbf{P} \cos nt + \mathbf{Q} \sin nt)$

E none of the above

7. A body falls under gravity against a resistance of kv^2 per unit mass, where v is the speed and k is a constant. After time t the body has fallen a distance s. Then

A $v\frac{dv}{ds} = g - kv^2$

B $v\frac{dv}{dt} = g + kv^2$

C $\frac{d^2s}{dt^2} = g + kv^2$

D $v\frac{dv}{ds} = -(g + kv^2)$

E $\frac{dv}{dt} = -g + kv^2$

8. A particle moves in the x–y plane so that its position vector $\mathbf{r}$ at time t seconds is given by $\mathbf{r} = (2t^2\mathbf{i} + t^3\mathbf{j})$m. When $t = 1$, the speed, in m s^{-1}, of the particle, is

A $\frac{3}{4}$

B $\sqrt{5}$

C 5

D 7

E 25

9. A particle P, of unit mass, moves under a resisting force $-k\mathbf{v}$, where k is a positive constant and $\mathbf{v}$ is the velocity of P. No other forces act on P, which has velocity $\mathbf{V}$ at time $t = 0$. At time t, $\mathbf{v}$ =

A $\mathbf{V}\, e^{kt}$

B $(\mathbf{V}/k)\, e^{kt}$

C $\mathbf{V}\, e^{-kt}$

D $(\mathbf{V}/k)\, e^{-kt}$

E $\mathbf{V}\,(1 - kt)$

10. A particle P of mass m is attached to a fixed point O by a light inextensible string of length a and describes vertical circles. When OP makes the angle θ with the downward vertical, the tension in the string is of magnitude T.

A $T - mg \cos \theta = ma\, \ddot{\theta}$

B $T - mg \cos \theta = ma\, \dot{\theta}^2$

C $T - mg \sin \theta = ma\, \ddot{\theta}$

D $T - mg \sin \theta = ma\, \dot{\theta}^2$

E $mg \cos \theta - T = ma\, \dot{\theta}^2$

SECTION II

Questions 11–15 **(Five questions)**

11. $\dfrac{d\mathbf{v}}{dt} = k\mathbf{v}$, where $k < 0$ and $\mathbf{v} \neq \mathbf{0}$.

1 $\dfrac{d^2\mathbf{v}}{dt^2} = k^2\mathbf{v}$

2 $\mathbf{v} \cdot \dfrac{d\mathbf{v}}{dt} < 0$

3 $\mathbf{v} \times \dfrac{d\mathbf{v}}{dt} = \mathbf{0}$

12.

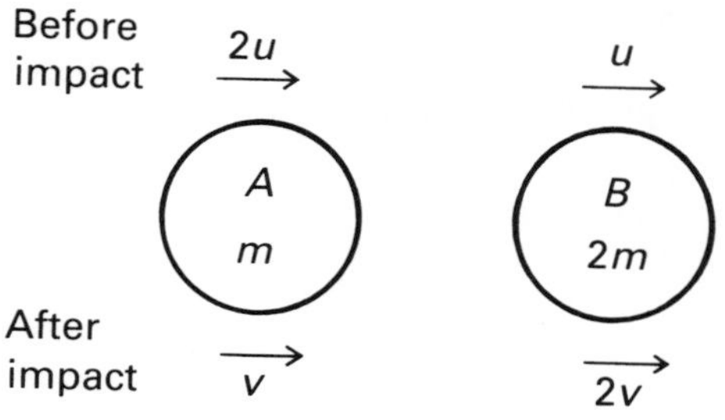

Two elastic spheres A and B, of masses m and $2m$ respectively, collide directly as shown.

1 $v = u$

2 The coefficient of restitution is 1

3 The kinetic energy before impact was $3mu^2$

13.

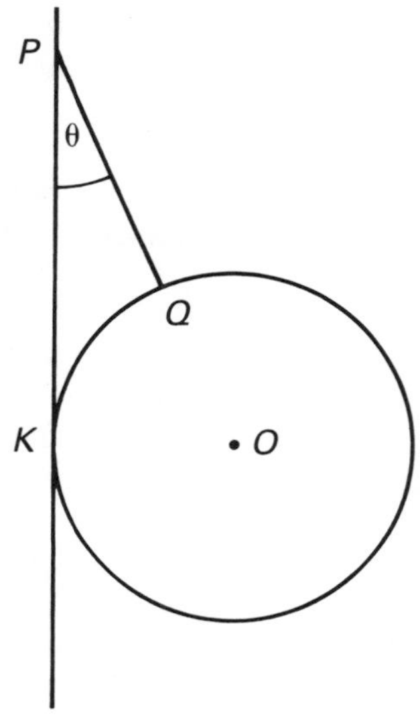

A uniform, solid, smooth sphere, with centre O and of radius a and mass m, is held in equilibrium and in contact with a smooth vertical wall by means of a light inextensible string PQ, of length a, attached to a point P on the wall and to a point Q on the surface of the sphere. The point of contact of the sphere and the wall is K and angle $KPQ = \theta$.

1 $\theta = \pi/6$

2 The tension in the string is of magnitude $2mg/\sqrt{3}$

3 The reaction between the wall and the sphere is of magnitude $mg\sqrt{3}$

14. Non-zero forces $3\mathbf{F}$ and $-4\mathbf{F}$ act at the points with non-zero position vectors $2\mathbf{a}$ and $-\mathbf{a}$ respectively. Their resultant $\mathbf{R}$ acts through a point with position vector $\mathbf{b}$.

1 $\mathbf{R} + \mathbf{F} = \mathbf{0}$

2 The moment of the system about the origin is $2\mathbf{a} \times \mathbf{F}$

3 An equation of the line of action of $\mathbf{R}$ is $\mathbf{r} = \mathbf{F} + t\mathbf{b}$

15. The position vectors of the points A, B, C, referred to the origin O, are $\mathbf{a}$, $\mathbf{b}$, $\mathbf{c}$ respectively. Given that $OABC$ is a parallelogram, then

1 $\mathbf{a} - \mathbf{b} + \mathbf{c} = \mathbf{0}$

2 the area of the parallelogram is $|\mathbf{a} \times \mathbf{b}|$

3 $\dfrac{\mathbf{a} \times \mathbf{c}}{\mathbf{a} \cdot \mathbf{c}}$ is a unit vector perpendicular to the plane of the parallelogram

SECTION III

Questions 16–20 **(Five questions)**

16. A rigid body is rotating about a fixed axis.

1 The moment of momentum of the body about the axis is increasing at a constant (non-zero) rate

2 The kinetic energy of the body is increasing at a constant (non-zero) rate

17. A uniform rod PQ, of mass m and length $2a$, is freely pivoted at P and hangs in equilibrium with Q vertically below P. The rod is then given an impulse at Q.

1 The initial speed of Q is $\sqrt{(2ag)}$

2 The initial kinetic energy of the rod is $mag/3$

18. A particle moves in a plane but not along a straight line.

1 The path of the particle is a circle and the magnitude of its velocity is constant

2 The acceleration of the particle is of constant magnitude

19. $\mathbf{p}$ and $\mathbf{q}$ are non-zero vectors.

1 $\mathbf{p} \times \mathbf{q} = \mathbf{0}$

2 $\mathbf{p} \cdot \mathbf{q} \neq 0$

20. X and Y are events.

1 $P(X \cap Y) = P(X) \cdot P(Y)$

2 $P(X|Y) = 0$

SECTION IV

Questions 21–25 **(Five questions)**

21. A rod PQ is free to oscillate in a vertical plane about a smooth horizontal axis through the end P. Find the period of small oscillations.

1 The moment of inertia of the rod about the axis is given

2 The distance of the centre of mass of the rod from P is given

3 The mass of the rod is given

4 The length of the rod is given

22. A particle is attached to one end of a spring whose other end is attached to a fixed point of a smooth horizontal table. The particle oscillates in a straight line on the table. Find the mass of the particle.

1 The period is given

2 The amplitude of the oscillations is given

3 The natural length of the spring is given

4 The modulus of the spring is given

23. A car is driven directly up a straight incline against a known frictional force. Find its acceleration at a particular instant.

1 The mass of the car is given

2 The speed of the car at that instant is given

3 The rate of working of the engine at that instant is given

4 The gradient of the incline is given

24. A particle is projected vertically downwards in a resisting medium. Find its terminal velocity.

1 The initial speed is given

2 The resistance is proportional to the speed

3 The mass of the particle is given

4 When the speed is 1 $m\,s^{-1}$ the resistance is given

25. A uniform cuboid, of mass M and edges of lengths a, b and c, is free to rotate about a vertical axis along one of the edges of length b. Find the moment of inertia of the cuboid about this axis.

1 M is given

2 a is given

3 b is given

4 c is given

SECTION V

Questions 26–30 **(Five questions)**

26. Find the probability that both events X and Y will occur.

1 $P(X|Y)$ is given

2 $P(X \cup Y)$ is given

27. A car of given mass m, initially moving with given speed V on a straight level track, is brought to rest by the brakes which exert a constant retarding force of magnitude F. Find F.

1 The car comes to rest in a given time T

2 The car comes to rest in a given distance S

28. A projectile fired from a point O on a horizontal plane just clears a vertical wall which is perpendicular to the plane of the projectile's trajectory. Find the distance of the wall from O.

1 The speed of projection is given

2 The height of the wall is given

29. Find the moment of inertia of the uniform square lamina $PQRS$ about a line which is perpendicular to the plane of the lamina and which passes through P.

1 The moment of inertia of the lamina about PQ is given

2 The moment of inertia of the lamina about PR is given

30. A bag contains just w white balls and r red balls. Two balls are to be drawn from the bag without replacement. Find the probability that they will both be white.

1 $w = 2r$

2 The total number of balls in the bag is given

Answer keys

	Test 1	Test 2	Test 3	Test 4	Test 5	Test 6	Test 7	Test 8	Test 9	Test 10	Test 11	Test 12	Test 13	Test 14
1	E	A	C	A	D	B	D	D	B	C	B	C	B	E
2	D	D	B	E	C	E	C	B	E	D	E	D	A	A
3	A	C	A	D	B	D	A	E	A	C	A	B	E	B
4	B	E	D	B	E	C	E	C	D	A	A	A	D	C
5	C	B	E	C	A	B	B	A	C	E	E	E	C	D
6	E	A	A	E	E	A	C	E	A	A	C	E	D	B
7	D	B	E	B	B	D	A	B	B	E	B	B	A	A
8	A	C	B	D	D	C	E	D	C	B	E	D	E	C
9	B	E	C	A	E	C	B	A	D	B	C	A	C	C
10	C	E	B	C	C	D	A	E	E	D	D	C	B	B
11	D	D	D	C	E	D	D	C	A	E	B	A	B	A
12	E	C	E	E	C	D	B	B	B	D	C	B	B	E
13	A	D	A	A	A	E	B	C	D	A	B	E	D	B
14	B	A	D	D	A	B	C	D	C	B	D	D	A	D
15	B	B	E	A	D	A	E	A	E	C	A	A	E	B
16	D	E	C	C	B	C	D	E	D	A	D	A	D	D
17	A	C	D	B	B	A	E	A	A	E	A	E	B	C
18	C	D	B	B	C	C	C	E	E	C	E	B	A	A
19	E	B	A	B	A	E	A	B	C	C	D	C	C	A
20	C	D	A	E	C	C	A	B	B	D	C	C	E	E
21	D	E	A	B	B	B	A	C	B	B	E	E	A	D
22	C	B	B	D	C	E	C	A	C	C	C	C	E	B
23	E	A	D	A	A	B	B	E	B	A	C	D	B	E
24	A	D	C	B	E	D	D	D	E	E	A	E	C	A
25	B	E	B	E	D	A	C	C	D	D	C	B	D	C
26	A	A	E	C	B	E	A	B	B	A	D	D	B	E
27	B	E	B	A	E	A	B	E	A	E	D	B	D	A
28	D	D	A	C	C	C	E	B	C	D	E	C	D	E
29	E	B	E	D	D	D	D	D	E	B	A	E	C	A
30	C	B	C	E	A	C	E	A	D	C	D	C	E	D